Geology and the local museum

Making the most of your geological collection

Simon J Knell
Keeper of Natural Sciences
Scunthorpe Museum and Art Gallery

Michael A Taylor
Assistant Keeper of Earth Sciences
Leicestershire Museums, Arts and Records Service

Area Museums Service for South Eastern England
Area Museum Council for the South West

LONDON: HER MAJESTY'S STATIONERY OFFICE

© Crown copyright 1989
First published 1989

ISBN 0 11 290459 9

HMSO publications are available from:

HMSO Publications Centre
(Mail and telephone orders only)
PO Box 276, London SW8 5DT
Telephone orders 01-873 9090
General enquiries 01-873 0011
(queuing system in operation for both numbers)

HMSO Bookshops
49 High Holborn, London WC1V 6HB   01-873 0011 (Counter service only)
258 Broad Street, Birmingham B1 2HE   021-643 3740
Southey House, 33 Wine Street, Bristol BS1 2BQ   (0272) 264306
9-21 Princess Street, Manchester M60 8AS   061-834 7201
80 Chichester Street, Belfast BT1 4JY   (0232) 238451
71 Lothian Road, Edinburgh EH3 9AZ   031-228 4181

HMSO's Accredited Agents
(see Yellow Pages)

and through good booksellers

British Library Cataloguing in Publication Data

A CIP catalogue record for this book is available from the British Library

Cover photograph: should children be allowed to touch mineral displays?

Contents

USING COLLECTIONS

Acknowledgments

Monica Price, University Museum, Oxford, was a major contributor on minerals throughout, especially in sections 6.5, 10.7, 12 and the Bibliography, and developed the classification and data in appendix 7. Contributions and photographs were also provided by Anne and David Bone, Chichester District Museum (20); Mike Branney (21); John Martin, Leicestershire Museums (appendices 4, 5 and 6); Andrew Mathieson, City of Bristol Museum and Art Gallery (19); Tom Sharpe, National Museum of Wales (22); Di Smith, Bath Geology Museum (23), and Don Steward, Stoke-on-Trent City Museum (15.4). The cover illustration was supplied by Dorking Museum, with the help of Simon Timberlake.

Mike Bishop, George Breeze, Gordon Chancellor, Chris Collins, Peter Crowther, Micky Curtis, Phil Powell and the Scottish National Portrait Gallery provided additional illustrations. Patty Banham, Rosemary Brind, Howard Brunton, Chris Collins, Michael Crane, Phil Doughty, Rosemary Roden, Mick Stanley, Geoff Tresise and Gill Weightman supplied many useful comments. We are grateful to all our contributors.

The Museums and Galleries Commission provided a Conservation Grant for the distribution of this book to Area Museum Council member museums and the Geologists' Association provided additional funding.

We would like to thank Crispin Paine, Director, Area Museums Service for South Eastern England (AMSSEE); Stephen Locke, formerly Executive Director, Area Museum Council for the South West (AMCSW); Penny Spencer, Curator, Scunthorpe Borough Museum; Patrick Boylan, Director, Leicestershire Museums Service; and the Geological Curators' Group, for their encouragement and support.

Simon Knell
Michael Taylor

Abbreviations

AMCSW	Area Museum Council for the South West
AMSSEE	Area Museums Service for South Eastern England
BGS	British Geological Survey
CING	Collections Information Network – Geology
FENSCORE	Federation for Natural Sciences Collection Research
GCG	Geological Curators' Group
HMSO	Her Majesty's Stationery Office
IMA	International Mineral Association
LEA	Local Education Authority
MDA	Museum Documentation Association
NCC	Nature Conservancy Council
NSGSD	National Scheme for Geological Site Documentation

Preface

This book is written for curators who are not geologists, and geologists who are not trained curators, who find themselves responsible for a geological collection: the situation with most British geological collections.

Many British museums have geological collections, dating from the height of their popularity in Victorian and Edwardian times, some of which have been neglected for many years. The museum profession is only now beginning to appreciate the potential value of these collections, mainly due to the work of the Geological Curators' Group (GCG) (see 3.1).

Most museums with geological collections do not have a permanent specialist geological curator for a variety of reasons – usually lack of finance but often the lack of awareness of the need for such a post. Some museums are too small. Others have collections in the charge of people who have geological but not curatorial expertise. These people may be volunteers or government training scheme workers. Teachers in schools, colleges, polytechnics and universities are often in charge of geological collections, whether or not these are housed in a 'museum'.

A few museums have sufficiently important geological collections and a large enough staff to justify acquiring their own specialist curator. They have not done so, perhaps because they do not fully appreciate their collections' potential. As a result these collections have been neglected. One reason is the lack of a simple guide suitable for non-specialists. We hope that this book will fill the gap. It aims to answer two main needs:

- How to look after and use your collection
- Where to get help and advice.

Because this book has to be short and simple, it concentrates on geology in a 'typical' small or medium-sized museum. It cannot cover every possible case and you may need more detail if, for example, you have an unusually large collection of valuable minerals. We therefore recommend two further sources of reference, one for general museum matters such as security, and one for specialist geological curation.

Crispin Paine, *The Local Museum: notes for amateur curators*, 2nd edition, AMSSEE, 1986 (Good for general museum matters, this is written for English museums but is still highly relevant to Scottish museums; the various differences of organisation and law are covered by Timothy Ambrose, *New museums: a start-up guide*, HMSO, 1987.)

C H C Brunton, T P Besterman and J A Cooper (eds), *Guidelines for the curation of geological materials*, published for the GCG as Miscellaneous Paper 17 by the Geological Society, 1985.

The Bibliography gives a classified and descriptive list of many other useful and relevant books available.

The geological collection

Finally, two pieces of advice: if you can't do it all at once, every little helps, and any improvement is better than none. Ask and ask again for more resources from your management and governing body. They probably don't realise that your geological service can be important and worthwhile.

Geology and museums

1 What is geology?

Geology is 'the study of the earth as a whole, its origin, structure, composition (including the development of life) and the nature and development of the processes which have given rise to its present form' (Whitten and Brooks, *The Penguin Dictionary of Geology*). Increasingly the term 'Earth Sciences' is being adopted to include geology and the related disciplines of climatology, soil science, oceanography, geomorphology and planetary science.

Geology in the news

Geology has its own terminology which is a descriptive language needed to remove ambiguity, but which can confound the non-specialist by making even the simplest ideas seem complex. Nevertheless, amateurs still make valuable contributions, not least in the objects they give to museums. Even after the arrival of new technology, progress in geology is still dependent on specimens, especially those in museum collections. At its best it is meticulous and objective study fuelled by imagination. For many people it retains the romance and excitement of its pioneering years, and regular discoveries seem to turn the science upside down.

Geology is of course all around us, not just beneath our feet but in buildings, roads and almost every type of manmade product. The very shape of the landscape is determined by geological processes.

2 The geological collection

2.1 Its nature

What is a geological collection? To the museum curator, it is essentially an assemblage of rocks, minerals and fossils. The definitions of these three groups have necessarily been adapted to take into account the diversity of museum collections and the specialisms which have developed. For example, 'fossils' include the unaltered remains of wild animals which are perhaps only centuries old, but the archaeologist deals with the (perhaps much older) bones of people and their domestic stock. Similarly, rock collections contain hard rocks like granites and marbles, natural 'soft rocks' such as clay and soil, as well as building stones, and rock-like industrial products such as brick and slag. They do not include worked flint or carved stonework. Minerals, usually crystalline, inorganic substances, for convenience also include organic compounds such as coal, oil and amber. Finally, extraterrestrial meteorites make rare additions to a few fortunate geological collections.

Together these make up the museum's geological collection. In the end it is the particular expertise of the staff or the overall organisation of the museum which determines whether an inlaid table or a jet necklace is part of the decorative art or geological collection.

The specimens themselves range from large slabs containing huge

Large slab-mounted ichthyosaurs

A finely preserved mineral

Ashford black marble vase

reptiles or groups of crystals to borehole cores drilled deep in the earth's crust in search of mineral wealth; from collections of individual bones from one animal to hand-sized specimens and microscope slides. These objects do not exist in isolation and their value is largely determined by the nature and extent of supporting documentation, whether in the form of museum registers, catalogues, indexes and specimen labels, or hidden in the details of packaging and arrangement. All this is in equal need of curation. Collectors' notebooks, maps, photographs and equipment are as important as the specimens themselves. In addition, some museums have specialist libraries containing books of great rarity.

Many museum geological collections predate the birth of the subject as a true science. Others reflect the history of its national and local development. They may contain specimens which were weathered naturally for centuries to reveal their details; such specimens can never again be collected.

2.2   Its importance

This is undoubtedly the question curators would most like answered. Although a true estimate of the value of a collection can only be made by subject specialists, a simple evaluation is not difficult. The two criteria for assessing the importance of a collection are the quality of the material it contains and the level of associated documentation. The following gives some idea of what is expected of the data accompanying old specimens:

LOCALITY:
General, *eg* Ipswich – *good*
Specific, *eg* OS: SK410445 *or* Cleggs Pit – *excellent*

STRATIGRAPHY:
General, *eg* Gault – *good*
Specific, *eg* Zone of *Hoplites dentatus or* 3 ft below surface – *excellent*

COLLECTOR:
Old label but no name – good (collectors can often be recognised by their labels)
Name and date, eg J W Bodger 3 March 1883 – *excellent*

Note that for the moment little value is put on a specimen having a name, as this can be added at any time, and that what is excellent for an old collection is a bare minimum for newly collected material. It is quite exceptional to find excellent documentation in all these categories. If, in addition, the collection is stored in its original cabinet with the collector's notebooks and correspondence, it is even more of a rarity, and likely to be of great value to the museum.

Assessing the quality of the specimens making up the collection is less easy. Aesthetic criteria cannot be relied upon – perfect ammonites may be plentiful in one bed but even the smallest fragment rare in another. The thin powdery coating covering a perfect crystal may be of greater interest than the crystal itself.

An old well-documented fossil

A collector's notebook is as important as his specimens

The best documented collections form good site, species or historical records and have many research uses, and they are also best for education and display. Collections with little or no data are still of display or educational value, including hands-on use. There is no need to despair over an apparent lack of data as named collections can be rediscovered (see 6.11) and documentation relating to old collections may exist in other museums.

Some material is so characteristic that a specialist may be able to assign locality and stratum. It is also necessary to consider a collection's future value, but as we cannot predict the direction research will take, nor what new technologies will allow us to extract from old material, this will always remain an unknown quantity.

It may be some time before the full importance of your collection is known as collections research is still at a very early stage, but the process can be accelerated by publicising the material and encouraging specialists to visit (see section 3).

3 Interested parties

3.1 The Geological Curators' Group

The GCG was founded in 1974 to improve the status of geology in museums and similar institutions, and to promote the proper curation of geological collections in general, including education and the conservation of specimens and sites. It holds meetings throughout the UK, provides information and advice, and is involved in the National Scheme for Geological Site Documentation (NSGSD). Anyone interested in the care of geological material is encouraged to join (see appendix 9).

In 1986 the Geological Curators' Group started the 'Collections Information Network – Geology' (CING) which attempts to summarise basic information on the content and state of every geological collection in the UK. It differs from the Collections Research Units (see 3.2) in being concerned also with the condition and use of the collection. Each collection which is reliably recorded is eventually briefly described in the CING column of the GCG's journal, *The Geological Curator*.

The Geological Curator, published three times a year, has articles about new developments, techniques, and individual collectors and museums, a section for topical news and regular book and exhibition reviews, as well as the CING column. The 'Lost and Found' section publishes requests for information about museums and collectors, and the resulting responses.

Your collection may well justify a feature article in the main pages of *The Geological Curator*, over and above the CING column. You may find a geological curator to write such a piece, especially after a survey of the collection, and you may want to collaborate by carrying out local research. Quite apart from the value of learning more about your own collection, this is a good way of making the collection known to curators and some amateur and academic geologists, and of stimulating further information.

Among the GCG's most notable publications are Philip Doughty's 1981 report *The state and status of geology in UK museums*, which exposed widespread neglect and decay, and Brunton, Besterman and Cooper (*op cit*).

National Scheme for Geological Site Documentation

The NSGSD operates a network of 50 museum-based Record Centres throughout the UK holding nearly 20,000 site records. This information is used by planning authorities, conservation bodies and researchers; to direct school and student parties away from vulnerable sites to worthwhile alterna-

Quarry site

tives; and inside the museums themselves, for displays, documentation and publications. Record Centres hold a great deal of information which may be useful to the small museum. See appendix 1 to find your local Record Centre.

'Thumbs Up'

The 'Thumbs Up' campaign was started by the GCG in 1985 with the aim of increasing the public profile of geology in museums. So far the scheme has produced an attractive and popular leaflet for children, 'Rocks, fossils and minerals; how to make the best of your collection', available free to museums, and the campaign will continue to develop.

The GCG has also listed museums providing a geological service, on a two-tier system. This list is printed on the back of the 'Thumbs Up' leaflet. First-tier museums have a specialist geological curator and are accredited with the 'Thumbs Up' sign which they can put up in their entrance. Second-tier museums do not have a specialist curator but are still listed if they provide displays, reference collections or identification services. (See appendix 9 for address.)

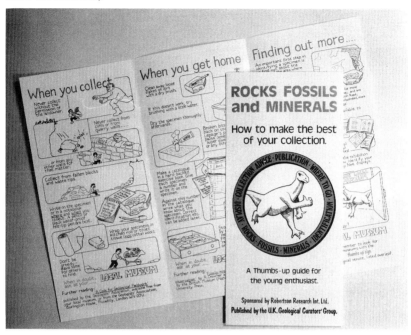

3.2 Natural Science Collections Research Units

During the 1970s geology and biology curators throughout the UK set up Collections Research Units (CRUs) to list named collections in their areas, including in museums without natural-science staff. A named collection can be one or more specimens owned or collected by a known person or institution. Together the CRUs formed FENSCORE, the Federation for Natural Sciences Collection Research, which processed the collected data at the Manchester Museum. The CRUs are mainly concerned with listing collections and perhaps the more important individual specimens, such as type specimens. Advice on the care and use of collections is not their primary aim. Contact your local CRU through your Area Museum Service (appendix 9), especially if you think your collection may have been missed or if you want a copy of the regional report.

3.3 Geology Today

Consider featuring your museum in the 'Museum File' series of *Geology Today*, a bimonthly magazine published in association with the Geological Society and the Geologists' Association (see appendix 9 for address). It is widely read by geologists in schools, colleges, universities, museums and amateur societies. This is particularly useful if your museum is in an area popular with field parties.

4 Taking action

You need to be fully informed about the content, quality and condition of your geological collection before you make any decision about it, even if you eventually decide to leave it alone! Your Area Museum Service is a valuable source of help, advice and funding. You should contact it if you have not already done so (see appendix 9).

4.1 The survey

The most useful action you can take before doing anything else is to have an experienced geological curator carry out a survey and write a report on the collection. It is very important to find the right person – an experienced geological curator who appreciates the problems and potential of small museums. Your Area Museum Service may have a Geological Officer to carry out such surveys. Otherwise, write to the Geological Curators' Group who will put you in touch with a suitable person (see 3.1).

The survey

The survey should assess the current situation, and any action needed, for every aspect of the collection:

- its contents
- its history and importance in the broadest sense (including scientific and historical importance)
- documentation
- storage
- accessibility of material, including organisation and arrangement of larger collections
- conservation and preparation needs and how they might be met
- actual and potential use in displays and other public services

- security problems, including insurance and health and safety matters
- how the museum fits in with other museums in the same area
- an outline of recommendations in rough order of priority, with brief comments on available resources including specialists (eg Area Museum Service conservation services), and the possible use of volunteers.

Unless your Area Museum Service operates a free service, expect to pay travel and subsistence costs and perhaps a daily rate for your surveyor, but this is money well spent, and financial help may be available from the Area Museum Service. The time needed to complete the survey will be determined by the size and storage of the collection. Before the surveyor comes, make sure that you know where everything is, and that it is accessible for the visit, if it is not normally so. Remember all documentation, files and books relating to the collection, and material stored in outstations. Send copies of any publications such as histories or catalogues concerning the museum to the surveyor in advance of the visit.

Meet the surveyor to discuss the background to the collections themselves, especially the resources available, and be on hand during the visit in case of problems or queries. Don't miss the chance of a personal demonstration of problems or points of interest.

The report should outline the main lines of action needed, and the time, skills and funds required. It must be used as a basis for further discussion and not as an end in itself. The final decision on what action to take can only be settled after further consideration of the resources, and the museum's general priorities. Your local knowledge here is as important as the surveyor's specialist knowledge.

If the local Area Museum Service is not providing a geological service or funds to help with geology in your area, and you think there is a need, then write and say so. They will not provide a service if there is no clear demand for one.

4.2   Deciding on a policy and plan

What are you going to do with your collection, and how will the museum be involved in geology?

With the museum's governing body, you will have to devise a general policy for geology in your museum in the light of the survey report and initial discussions.

A good policy for any museum without geological staff might be to provide a basic service covering the geology of the area but to leave more advanced services to a nearby county or other large museum with a specialist. Other options are disposal of the collections to another museum, or expansion of the service by recruiting a professional geological curator.

Once you have a policy, you will need to decide your strategy. For example, a policy which leaves specialist services to other museums implies that the museum itself will provide basic displays and some publications. The museum will still need to improve the storage and documentation of its existing collection, with some outside specialist help. However, site recording, identification services and new collecting, which all need specialist knowledge, will be left to other museums.

If your collection is disordered or dirty then you must give a high priority to its curation and conservation. It is comparatively useless until it is cleaned and curated. You also need to know what specimens you have, and what information there is about each, before you can use them to best effect.

Ideally curation and conservation should take place before anything else. In practice it can be a good idea to set up small temporary displays before finishing the work behind the scenes, which might itself be a good subject. This gives immediate results and an idea of the final benefits. It is also good for public interest and staff morale!

What next?

To sum up, ask yourself three questions:

1 Is the existing collection safe and accessible for use (that is, not deteriorating, orderly, secure, properly documented)? If not, can your museum put time and resources into at least basic rescue curation? If this is not obviously possible, should the collection be disposed of to a museum which can look after it, or would this be a major loss to the local museum? Would long loan be a better option if you cannot immediately do anything with your collection?

13

2 Do you want to operate any public service which needs in-house geological expertise, such as new collecting, site recording, specimen identification, and so on? If so, you will need to recruit a specialist geological curator. Or are you happy to have a basic service of displays and associated events (as described in sections 14–23)?

3 Would a compromise solution be best? Could you recruit a specialist curator for a limited period (say, 1–3 years) to clear the backlog of curatorial work and produce new displays? This will help you judge public interest once the collections are being used for something nearer their potential, and decide whether it is worth making the geologist's job permanent. Even if you don't get a permanent geologist at the end of the contract, the collection should have been properly curated and stored and is then much easier for a non-geologist to look after. If you have only a limited number of staff, think about getting a geologist next time a vacancy comes up.

Always remember that although you may not yourself be interested in geology, many people are. Indeed, the competence of anyone running a museum is best judged by how well one looks after the collections outside one's own field of interest.

4.3 Finding help

Finding the right help can be a problem. It is not possible to rely entirely upon volunteers, training scheme workers or vacation students – even if they have geological knowledge, they are usually inexperienced in museum work. Experienced geological curators are in short supply and can often spare only limited time, but you should try to find one to provide periodic supervision and advice.

The use of untrained workers, whether paid or unpaid, is not without problems. Benefits include involving people with their local museum, often teaching them something new while they give the museum the benefit of their work, local knowledge and moral support. The very character of the museum is, of course, often founded on the work of local volunteers. Disadvantages are the real dangers that the quality of the museum's work could suffer, and that damage could be done to the specimens and records. The workers will also be frustrated if faced with jobs which are too big or difficult, or too simple and mundane.

A good employment training or voluntary scheme can be beneficial to everyone involved, but the value of an undisturbed collection can be very quickly destroyed by overenthusiastic and ill-directed workers. In any case you need specialist supervision and advice, so get that first.

Remember, and guard against, the risk of theft by paid and unpaid workers (section 11). Many amateur geologists already have a keen personal interest in collecting and perhaps selling specimens. Among the most difficult thefts to uncover and solve are those where the thief has been curating the collection and its records.

Specialist geological curators

These are best found through your Area Museum Service. If it does not provide its own geological service or cannot help, try the GCG (section 3.1). It may be possible to offer temporary employment to an unemployed curator but do make sure that the salary and length of contract are reasonable.

If you decide to employ your own professional curator or anyone with equivalent responsibility over the collection, seek advice from your Area Museum Service or from the GCG and ensure that a professional geological curator is involved in *all* stages of the recruitment procedure, including the decision as to whether one is needed. In general, aim to recruit someone who has demonstrable understanding and experience of museum work, not just academic qualifications in geology.

Geologists

These may be amateurs, local society members, local teachers, university lecturers, vacation students, or unemployed graduates. They are almost always inexperienced in museum work, particularly curation and conservation, but could help with work such as guided walks, events and perhaps identifications. They may also be able to produce displays, although effective displays need a further input of specialist museum expertise in their composition and design. But they should not be left to make curatorial decisions: for example, they commonly throw away old and 'wrong' labels – always a disastrous mistake. Day to day supervision by a professional curator is essential, with occasional visits from a specialist geological curator.

4.4 Funding the work

There are many possible sources of funds for geological projects. Most important are the Area Museum Services, few of which get many requests for grant-aid for geology projects. The Museums and Galleries Commission has funded a number of curation and conservation projects. The Geologists' Association has funds available for small projects. It may also be worth approaching the Geological Society and, for scientifically important collections, the Royal Society. If a government scheme is to be used then money could be supplied for materials such as racking or stationery.

Few, if any, grant-awarding trusts provide money specifically for geology but you should certainly approach organisations with more general aims, especially in museums or education. See the *Museums Yearbook* and the *Museums Bulletin* and *Museums Journal* produced by the Museums Association. If you purchase specimens, a grant towards the cost of their purchase (or transport and installation, especially for large items like sets of dinosaur footprints) may be available from the grant-in-aid funds operated by the Science Museum and (in Scotland) the Royal Museum of Scotland. Also consider the National Heritage Memorial Fund. (However, you should think twice about acquiring scientifically important or unique specimens if you do not have a specialist curator to look after them.)

Are there any local trusts or bodies concerned with your area? Does your project have any particular relevance to a body whose work is not mainly concerned with museums? For example, guided walks or booklets will interest the local authority and civic society as well as countryside and conservation organisations.

Finally there is the possibility of obtaining sponsorship, which may not be as difficult as it first appears.

See appendix 9 for addresses: most of these bodies get very few applications related to geology and will be delighted to receive enquiries.

4.5 Making your service known

You will already be involved in publicising the museum as a whole, but you should also think about the needs of people interested in geology. A perennial problem of geologists using museums is to find out what collections exist and where. You should make sure that your collection is known to the several schemes which have tried to meet this need (see section 3). Get copies of the information held. If your collection is surveyed by a specialist curator, take the opportunity to check and correct previously reported information.

Care of collections

5 Approaches to new and old material

5.1 Collecting

You may want to collect even though there is no geologist on your staff. It may be that there are no geologists or other museums in your area and you fear that material will be lost. There is really no problem with this provided that you are aware of, and can provide, the necessary resources of time and knowledge. You must also have a collecting policy.

The collecting policy

There is insufficient space here to go into the benefits of having a collecting policy but it is a valuable guide to curator, trustee and public alike. The essential elements for a policy covering geological material are:

1 Restrict collecting to a specific geographical area.
2 Restrict collecting to material which has good stratigraphic (except perhaps in the case of minerals) and locality information. Avoid passively collecting poorly documented items brought in as enquiries. Chase up documentation where it appears to be inadequate.
3 Recognise your limitations in terms of time, space, materials and knowledge and liaise with local museum geologists where possible. Be prepared to pass on your more important finds to a museum which is better able to use and care for them.
4 Try to get local amateur geologists to identify new finds, if necessary, so that material is rapidly processed and a backlog does not develop.
5 If you don't know what you're collecting don't collect.
6 Avoid developing specialisations such as a concentration on ammonites unless this is justified by the local geology.
7 Collect separately for school loans purposes.
8 Do not collect material from overseas.
9 Liaise with neighbouring museums to decide who collects what and from where, and whether in fact you need to collect at all.

Receipt of new material

Keep an eye on newly acquired material (see section 10 for possible conservation problems) and do not have it consolidated unless it appears to be deteriorating, then act fast. When in doubt consult a specialist.

1 Wet bones, horns, tusks and teeth need to be soaked thoroughly in clean water and allowed to dry slowly. Use polythene sheeting and dishes of water to create an environment of high humidity to slow the drying process. Keep an eye open for mould growth. Damp or dry material of this type should not be washed; allow any dampness to dry out slowly (see 10.5 and 10.6).

2 Dry wet minerals slowly. Do not wash minerals.

3 Non-friable material collected from the coast should be washed in several changes of water to remove salt. Dry slowly (see 10.3).

5.2 Restoring old collections

Many old collections exist today in a state of neglect and decay. While this, if left uncorrected, will lead to their eventual destruction, ill-considered restoration can be equally destructive. Curatorial expertise is initially more important than geological knowledge, and these are projects which must not be left to inexperienced staff. If you come across an old collection it is always worth contacting a professional geological curator (see 4.3).

There are two main problems associated with poorly restored collections. The first is the loss of information contained in old packaging material or

Unpacking a collection

labels. The second is the introduction of ambiguity by mixing old collections or failing to distinguish between inferred and recorded information. The schedule listed below is designed to avoid these problems and to enable a collection to be curated to a basic level.

1 Before work begins gather together all relevant documentation – accession records, catalogues, notebooks, indexes, letters, annual reports, etc. Is it the collection of one person, more than one person, or the museum as a whole? Who were the collectors? Who last worked on the collection and when? Why is it in its present condition? Is it organised or ordered in any way?

2 Look at the outside of the boxes or crates. Do they have any distinctive marks, labels, numbers, etc? Are any of the same design? Treat individual drawers in cabinets in the same way.

3 If you have found that the collection has an order then work through it in that order, otherwise allocate a number to each box or drawer. Create a list and for each box note its type, eg wood, card, 'Acme Biscuits', etc, and any external markings, eg 'L.G.S.', ' "A" in circle in red crayon', 'Parkinson Coll.'

4 Open one box or drawer at a time and add to your list details of packaging materials, eg 'wrapped in *Daily Chronicle* dated 4 October 1933'.

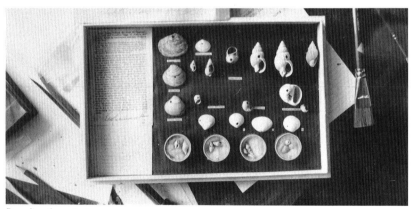

Recording the contents

5 As you unwrap each specimen and transfer it to a new container check the wrapping paper for pencilled locality information, names, numbers, etc. Keep an eye open for any specimen labels, especially tiny number tags which may have become detached from the specimen. Deal with one specimen at a time and keep all labels, including those written on wrappings (cut them off), with the specimens. Keep all specimens and loose labels from one box or drawer together.

6 After each box or drawer has been emptied ask yourself why were these specimens in the same box? Same collector, locality, geological age, or label design? All fossils? and so on. Add this information to your list.

7 Note any conservation problems (see section 10). Treat labels which have no specimens as though they did have specimens – you will want to know what has been lost or destroyed, or you may find the specimen to which the label belongs.

8 When all the boxes or drawers have been emptied the list should give some indication of how the collection was originally stored and how it should be organised in its new storage.

9 As the collection is reorganised transfer any details from your list onto the specimen labels and registers (see 6.4) if it is likely that this information will be lost during reorganisation. Where information has been inferred then say so, using square or double brackets (see 6.4) and say why, eg '[? Folkestone] (in box with specimens from there)' '[? Spencer Perceval Coll.] (same green label)'.

10 Write a few notes on how you found and restored the collection, ideally with photographs, and put them and the lists in a history file (see 6.3 and 6.4).

6 Documentation

6.1 Introduction

Documentation has two main aims:
- to audit the collection, and account legally for every item in the museum's custody
- to link each item with associated data, especially provenance.

Documentation also allows the provision of a detailed catalogue with all known information about each item, and a set of indexes listing specimens under various headings.

The priorities are to number and list specimens. The documentation of a geological collection differs little from that of other collections in the museum. If you have not already considered the documentation system of your museum as a whole, now is a sensible time. Advice on documentation in general is available from your Area Museum Service and from the Museum Documentation Association (MDA) (see appendix 9). Discuss the documentation of your geological collection with a specialist curator if you are in doubt.

Documenting the collection

Computers are only really useful for the preparation of catalogues, indexes and labels. The average microcomputer is not reliable or secure enough to be used as the only listing of specimens and you should keep back-up copies on disc and get a regular printout on paper. The range of computers and programs is always changing and you will need to seek advice from your Area Museum Service, the MDA, and the independent Museums' Computer Group (appendix 9). The MDA markets programs designed for museums, but ordinary commercial databases may suit your needs. The Museums' Computer Group may be able to direct you to a museum which can show a particular system in operation.

After completing your initial lists you must then decide on your needs regarding indexes and catalogues (section 6.6). These could be compiled manually (using MDA Cards), or on a computer. The work put into filling in paper cards could just as well be put into entering the same information onto a computer database, which is easier to maintain and has greater flexibility. You can then use it to make regular lists of specimens sorted by different criteria (eg by species or by age), or you can make on-line searches for particular words.

6.2   The documentation system

The basic system

Geological specimens come into the museum as individual accessions each ranging from a single specimen to an entire collection. The museum also acquires unpublished documents such as field notes, letters, site descriptions and photographs, all relevant to specimens in the collections. Three kinds of information thus have to be recorded:

- accession data, to prove legal title and record acquisitions; each accession may be an individual specimen or group of specimens, with its own accession number recorded in an accessions register
- specimen data about individual specimens; each specimen has its own number, recorded in a specimen register or MDA Extension Sheet
- relevant documents such as letters and publications, usually kept in numbered history files.

This is a basic documentation system. Detailed catalogues and indices are optional extras.

Which system to use

If the existing system is fairly complete and working well, and conforms to the data standard (see below), don't waste time on replacing it unnecessarily.

23

If existing documentation is lacking or poorly maintained, you will probably have to start afresh, salvaging what information you can. Whichever system you adopt, you should ensure that it conforms to the Museum Documentation System published by the MDA. This consists of a data standard – a standardised way of setting down information – and a range of stationery and computer software based on the data standard. A basic system consists of entry forms, an accessions register, indexes, specimen tags or marking, a catalogue, specimen labels and history files. The first four are requirements of the Museum Registration Scheme.

Whatever system you use, write a report outlining it so that anyone else working on the collection can continue in the same way.

6.3 What materials to use

You may already use documentation stationery, such as that supplied by the MDA, for the general operation of your museum. However, you will still need some materials for the geological collection.

Tags and labels

You will need:

Tags to number the specimens. Tags can simply be numbered by hand on plain acid-free paper of good quality (about 60 gsm). However, it is useful to have pre-printed paper, using either the MDA code for the museum or a shortened version of its name (which may mean more to non-museum people). Never use self-adhesive labels as tags; the adhesive deteriorates and the labels fall off. The alternative is to mark specimens directly, but see 6.4.

Specimen labels to hold basic information about, and be kept with, the specimen. Specimen labels should be printed on good quality acid-free thin card (not paper), trimmed to fit easily inside the card trays used by the museum (section 7.3). It is useful to have two sizes of specimen label for large and small specimens.

If you have only a small geological collection you may prefer to use a more general 'museum object' label.

Comments labels for further comments about specimens.

Accessions registers, entry and exit forms and transfer of title forms

You should already have a central accessions system for your museum. We recommend the MDA's Accessions Register, Entry and Exit Forms and Transfer of Title Forms. If you use your own accessions register, it should be a bound ledger of lined acid-free archival paper.

Name *Asteroceras*
stellare

Horizon *Frodingham*
Ironstone, Lower Jurassic

Locality *Conesby Mine,*
Scunthorpe,
Humberside

Collection *H.E. Dudley*

Reg. No. . . . . . . Ac. No *1939.41*

Remarks *Identified by*
Dr. Spath. March 1942.

. . . . . . Gallery & Museum

University
Mus. Oxford *1987.41.4*
Geol.

University
Mus. Oxford *1987.41.6*
Geol.

University
Mus. Oxford *1987.50*
Geol.

Loaned to

Loan No.

Date returned . . . . Date

Remarks

Geology File . . . . Reg. No.

Name *Proustite*

Remarks *Initials 'DJB' on specimen*
may refer to DJ Bunny the
(19a mineral dealer and
collector (see history file).

Determined by *C.J. Collins*

Date *10.1988* Reg. No. *1898.413.6*

194CM/260 P&S

Specimen number tags; specimen label; specimen on loan label and comments label

25

Specimen registers and extension sheets

We recommend the MDA Extension Sheets. If you use a separate specimen register, it should be a bound ledger of lined acid-free archival paper.

History files

History files can simply be foolscap acid-free archival envelopes, ideally opening along the long side and either pre-printed or stamped with a custom-made rubber stamp with the name of the museum, and a space for the number and brief title:

> Barchester Museum
> History File
> Title: 1882.233 *Plesiosaurus*, Lower Lias, Framley, donated by Archdeacon Grantly

History files are usually stored in accession number order, but when sorting through old correspondence etc it can be useful to set up three runs: one for subject, one for collector (or other named person) and a third for individual specimens arranged in accession and specimen number order. If an item relates to more than one file, put a photocopy or a note of the location of the original in the other file.

Pen, ink, pencil and varnish

Always use a good quality pen with high quality permanent black Indian ink, such as that produced by Rotring. If you want to make a temporary note use pencil. Never use ballpoint or felt-tip pens for museum records or displays as they fade very quickly.

Get a supply of artist's acrylic varnish. This is waterproof but can be removed with solvent if necessary.

6.4 How to document a specimen

Accession the specimen or group of specimens Give it an accession number linking it with its accession documentation such as the MDA Transfer of Title Form and Entry Form. Complete the forms and the accessions register. Under the MDA system the accession number consists of a consecutive number prefixed by the year of accession:

> 1988.28 mammoth tooth, Sandford gravel pit . . .
> 1988.29 collection of Cornish minerals . . .

Number each individual specimen A collection of specimens will have the same accession number:

1988.29 collection of Cornish minerals (23 specimens)

Individual specimens are usually numbered by 'extension number' suffixes:

1988.29.1 quartz with mica, Cligga Head . . .

1988.29.2 hematite, Botallack . . .

A common problem is a specimen whose accession details are lost. Enter it as newly accessioned this year, but 'found in store'. Unfortunately, if you ever match it with the original accession, it now has two different accession numbers; note this at both places in the accessions register.

If your museum uses separate accession and specimen numbers, then follow much the same rules as above, but leave blank the accession number if this is not known:

Acc. No.	Spec. No.	Item
1988.29.3	2336	cassiterite, Wheal Jane [new accession]
1903.1	2337	hematite [old specimen, accession known]
[blank]	2338	ichthyosaur tooth . . . [found in store, history as yet unknown]

Treat associated pieces of one specimen as a single specimen:

- two matching blocks with the fossil between them ('part and counterpart')
- the bones of one skeleton
- the pieces of a specimen which can't for some reason be glued together (including research samples such as thin sections).

Record each piece under the same specimen number then give it its own number suffix separated by a clearly written full stop (or stroke):

1987.115 Partial skeleton of dinosaur *Scelidosaurus*
    1987.115.1 Femur
    1987.115.2 Tibia

Number the specimen Number and cut out a tag, let the ink dry, and stick it on the worst side of the specimen with HMG glue. Once dry, varnish it to seal it. Tiny specimens are best placed in special containers which are themselves labelled. Alternatively, you can write on the specimen, but only if you are sure you won't disfigure it. For this reason, do not use white paint as a background on which to write.

Record the information about the specimen on the label, and in the extension sheet or specimen register You should record as much as possible (see 6.5) of:

specimen number (if separate one used)

accession number

identification

horizon

locality

collector/donor and date (note that 'collector' can mean either the finder or the owner of a specimen)

other notes (including where in the museum the specimen was found, if part of an old collection; if the specimen is published; weight of gemstones and meteorites (for security and identification); etc.

For recording details of old specimens, it is usually adequate to transcribe from existing labels (see 6.5).

There are two rules to follow:

- When you record something, be sure to make any inferences clear. This avoids spurious certainty in your records, and allows future workers to make their own assessments. The usual method is to put square brackets around any inference. If you are using a typewriter or computer without square brackets, use double round ones.

    eg A. S. [?Arthur's Seat] or A. S. ((?Arthur's Seat))

- If you make a mistake, delete it by drawing two neat lines through it. Do not obliterate it with ink or correcting fluid. This is to avoid the risk of alterations being made to hide loss or theft.

Keep all old labels Number each loose label neatly with the specimen number and place it either in a small selfseal polythene bag with the specimen, or in the history file relating to the specimen. Alternatively, old labels can be stored in albums of appropriate quality heavy paper or, better still, hinged to this paper in Secol or equivalent wallets in bound books. Small labels are then far less likely to be accidentally lost. Treat old labels without specimens as if they were specimens. You may find the specimen in due course; otherwise, it serves as a record of what has been lost from the collection.

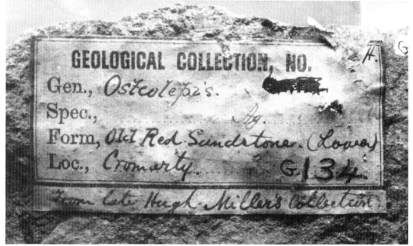

Old specimen label

Put documents in a history file Documents relating to the accession, such as entry forms, go in a history file marked and filed under the accession number. Documents concerning the individual specimen, such as old labels, correspondence, and copies of publications, go in a history file marked with the accession number with the extension suffix to indicate the specimen.

6.5 What to record

Identification

As a non-geologist you may be concerned at the thought of having to cope with specialist terms and identifying and classifying specimens. This seems complicated by changes in terminology: your museum specimens have 'old' names and you may not have the books or expertise to know the 'new' names.

Don't worry. These are not serious problems. It is more important for you to record the specimen's exact provenance, especially where it came from originally and where it was found in the museum. This information will be lost if you do not preserve it, whereas a specimen can be identified or classified at any time. If you can classify the specimen to the best of your ability, so much the better (see appendices 2 to 7 and the Bibliography), otherwise just leave it as 'geological specimen'.

Fossils

Fossils are the ancient remains of animals and plants and their traces (eg footprints). Each species is given a name in two parts, the genus followed by the species name, then the authors of the species and finally the date when they published their description of the species (these last two are often omitted):

Ammonites bifrons Bruguière 1789 – or just *Ammonites bifrons*

Note that the genus is written with a capital letter and the species without. Both should be underlined or printed in italics.

If a later palaeontologist decides that the species should be put in a different genus, the author and date are placed in brackets:

Hildoceras bifrons (Bruguière 1789)

But the old name is still correct. Simply be sure to record both old and new names. Don't worry if a geologist suggests that you have the 'wrong' names, but record these new opinions with the person's name on the specimen label or a comments label, the history file, and of course any index or catalogue. Don't cross out the old names.

Identifying specimens needs familiarity with the idiosyncracies of fossilisation and weathering. You will also need to know which parts are actually used for identification. Books usually show perfect specimens which often seem very different from the actual specimen in your hand! Sometimes the parts needed for identification are damaged or hidden.

There are so many species of fossil that you will not always be able to identify a specimen to species or even genus level. Vertebrates are a particular problem as each species contains many often very differently shaped teeth and bones.

If you cannot identify a fossil further than a particular level because of lack of knowledge, then just leave it at that. Sometimes a specimen is too poorly preserved for a full identification, and the partial identification is suffixed by 'indet.' (for indeterminate). An uncertain identification is then prefixed by a question mark:

> trilobite (not taken further due to lack of knowledge)
> trilobite indet. (known to be a trilobite but too poorly preserved to say what kind)
> ? marcasite

Do try to build up a small library of general identification books, and books and papers relevant to the geology of your area (see the Bibliography). If any of your specimens are published (see 6.8), make sure you have copies of all publications – visitors will want to use them in connection with the specimens.

Minerals

Minerals are naturally occurring solid substances of inorganic origin. Each mineral has a distinctive and orderly arrangement of atoms, and a chemical composition which varies only between narrow limits. When a mineral has been able to grow freely during formation, it typically has crystals with flat faces. This is a consequence of its orderly atomic structure.

Minerals are identified and classified according to their chemical composition and crystal structure. Each mineral species may come in more than one variety. Unlike fossils, mineral species are not capitalised or underlined in writing. However, always put the variety name (if used) after the species name:

quartz var. amethyst

Many different names have been used for minerals in the past. The accepted name for each species is now agreed by an international commission. Appendix 7.2 lists the commoner synonyms as well as other substances commonly found in mineral collections, including organic compounds, mixtures, rocks, general names, and discredited or unacceptable species and variety names. Use it to find the currently acceptable name. If the synonym is not there, it should be in Hey's *Index* or its appendices (Bibliography).

When registering a specimen, always record all names found on specimen labels or other documentation. If possible, cite the current name for the main entry, especially for labels, indexes and catalogues. Look up the current name in appendix 7.2 and use it but only if you can attribute it with certainty. If in doubt, record the old name in single round brackets as original data, after the acceptable name. If you are uncertain about the identity of a specimen, store it at the end of the collection to await identification. Keep a record of the old name, together with old labels etc, in a history file.

If a collection is labelled with 'chemical' names such as 'sulphuret of copper', you need expert help in reidentifying it.

Mineral identification is difficult for the inexperienced as each mineral can come in various crystal forms and colours. However, it can be useful to find out more about a specimen which is already labelled. See the Bibliography for some useful guides: if you cannot make a clear identification with these, then you need expert help.

Rocks

Rocks are first classified by the manner in which they were formed, as sedimentary, metamorphic or igneous rocks. Group them by lithology (eg sandstone, limestone, etc) and then geographical location or stratigraphy. If you have a suite of rocks from a particular locality it is best to keep them together. It is generally best to use guides to local geology (see the Bibliography) to find the name but when in doubt just record what is known.

Locality

The locality is the place where a specimen was found. For old specimens, record it as a straight transcription of the label and records. Do not infer or add information unless you are really familiar with the geology of the area. Beware of localities with similar names; names may also have been used vaguely, eg Whitby for several miles of the Yorkshire coast.

For new collections, of course, be as accurate as possible, and if you know the precise location record the National Grid Reference (see any Ordnance Survey map to find out how to do this).

Meteorites are named after the place where they fell.

Horizon

The horizon is the rock stratum or layer from which a specimen came. For old specimens, the terminology used has changed so much over the years that you should again transcribe exactly what is on the label or in the records.

Mineral specimens rarely have horizon data. Sometimes the mine and even level are recorded.

Even if you are familiar with stratigraphy, do not convert to modern terminology without using square brackets or comments to make the inference clear. For new specimens be as accurate as possible. If you have geological expertise available always record the horizon, age and period using the standard British stratigraphy published in the series of *Special Reports of the Geological Society of London*. Appendix 2 is a simplified version.

Collector and donor

This could be the person who found the specimen or who later owned it. This information may be recorded on existing labels or found by further research (6.11).

6.6 Indexes and detailed catalogues

You will need an index to gain full access to your records. An index lists selected and abbreviated data in a particular order, usually one index each for specimen type, geological age, collector and locality. An index can be a set of index cards, a computer printout or an interactive computer system which can search for whatever you type in.

A detailed catalogue such as a completed MDA Card records almost all the known information about a specimen. However, for most museums much of this information is not really necessary; for example, there is little point in recording the colour and size of most specimens (except semi-precious minerals and gems).

Full indexes and detailed catalogues take a long time to complete, and need specialist knowledge to convert information to a consistent standard terminology. If this is not done, the index will be useless. For example, it is no good looking under 'pyrite' or 'Lias' for specimens entered under 'fool's gold' or 'Lower Jurassic'.

Before you start an index or catalogue, check the following points:

- Do not start an index unless basic listing, labelling, curation and storage of the collection have been completed. (The exception is when you are using a computer to produce the lists.)

- Which indexes do you need? The physical arrangement of the collection should act as its own index under at least one classification. An index is essential for large collections, or smaller collections which are hard to look through (but in the latter case you would be better spending the time improving the storage and arrangement of the collection).

- Can you keep the catalogue up to date with new specimens, conservation treatments, publications, and so on? You must also be able to maintain the indexes you create (see 6.9).

- Do you have sufficient access to specialist knowledge and the geological literature to prepare a reasonably reliable index and catalogue? If you don't, the result will be incomplete and even misleading.

However, you should certainly have an index and catalogue, even if it's only a handlist, for published specimens (type, figured and cited material, section 6.8). Visiting specialists can help here. Catalogues may be worthwhile for other collections of unusual historic or scientific interest. Consult a specialist curator.

It is unusual to publish catalogues of an entire collection but catalogues of interesting parts, particularly published specimens, are commonly published in the county society proceedings, or as part of an account of the museum in *The Geological Curator.*

6.7 Using the MDA Card

Many museums use a set of MDA Cards, but we do not recommend them if you are starting a new documentation system. They duplicate information which should already be recorded in the accessions register and extension sheet. Provided it conforms to the MDA data standard, a simpler card or computer index may be of more use and quicker to construct. Often proper accessioning is bypassed and the MDA Card forms the only record of a specimen. This is a major security risk as cards are easily lost or removed.

You may decide to use the MDA Card if your collection has already been documented using it. If so, you should use the MDA's *Geology specimen card*

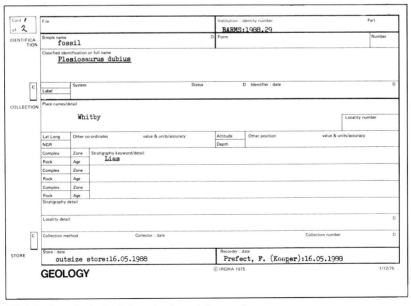

MDA Card completed using information from existing records

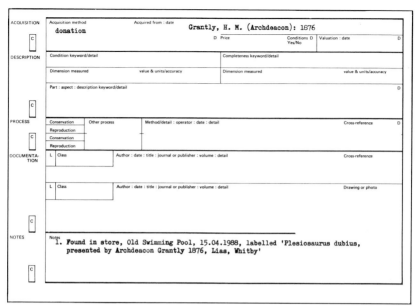

ACQUISITION	Acquisition method	Acquired from : date		Grantly, H. M. (Archdeacon): 1876				
[C]	donation			D Price		Conditions D Yes/No	Valuation : date	D
DESCRIPTION	Condition keyword/detail			Completeness keyword/detail				
	Dimension measured		value & units/accuracy	Dimension measured			value & units/accuracy	
	Part : aspect : description keyword/detail							D
[C]								
PROCESS	Conservation	Other process	Method/detail : operator : date : detail				Cross-reference	D
[C]	Reproduction							
	Conservation							
	Reproduction							
DOCUMENTA-TION	L	Class	Author : date : title : journal or publisher : volume : detail				Cross-reference	
	L	Class	Author : date : title : journal or publisher : volume : detail				Drawing or photo	
NOTES	Notes							
[C]	1. Found in store, Old Swimming Pool, 15.04.1988, labelled 'Plesiosaurus dubius, presented by Archdeacon Grantly 1876, Lias, Whitby'							

The reverse side of the MDA Card

instructions. Do not try to fill in the entire card for each specimen. Only fill in what you are sure of and leave the rest blank. The following notes will help in completing the card to a basic level:

Identification simple name only, or transcribe from label

Collection enter label data exactly and note that collector here means the person who actually found the specimen. In the Stratigraphy section, do not qualify the details by crossing out the Complex-Rock-Zone-Age boxes.

Store location only if necessary (ie your specimen is out of the main sequence), date.

Acquisition all details possible.

Description best ignored in favour of looking at the specimen, but note weight etc for valuable items (see section 12).

Process as necessary, eg if specimen is sampled or conserved.

Documentation if anything known, especially if specimen has a history file or is a published specimen.

Notes Any other details of specimen, label and provenance, especially where it was found in the museum.

6.8 Published specimens

Specimens which have been published in the scientific literature must be recorded and marked. They are important as present and future workers will want to see them and check the conclusions based on these specimens. Give priority to their care and security. If you cannot do so, consider transfer to a more secure institution (section 10).

It is important to appreciate that any old collection may contain such specimens, often not marked as such, and sometimes quite unimpressive at first sight. Finding missing published specimens can be difficult, even if they are illustrated, since the drawings may have been reversed or cropped, or the specimens may have been altered since then. It may be necessary to reserve final judgment and mark specimens as 'possible type', etc.

It is equally important to appreciate that many unpublished specimens in museums can become just as valuable once they have been written up by a modern specialist.

Type specimens are the most important, since they are the actual reference specimens on which species of fossil animals and plants and also minerals are based. They are unique and irreplaceable. There are various kinds of type specimen but all are important (except perhaps 'topotypes' which merely come from the same locality as the original type). Mark the specimen, label and register entry with a green paper dot.

Figured specimens are those which have been illustrated in a scientific paper. Mark the specimen, label and register entry with a green paper dot.

Cited specimens have been individually described or mentioned. Mark the specimen, label and register entry with a red paper dot.

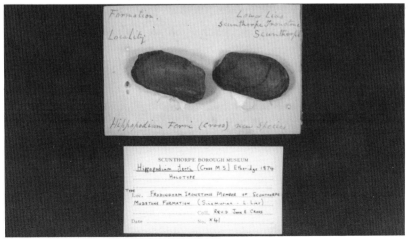

Holotype

6.9 Maintaining the system

Keep records up to date. Add new acquisitions or specimens found in the store. Also add new information to existing documentation when specimens have been reidentified, conserved, loaned, published or put on display. Note this in the register, and on extension sheets, specimen labels and comments labels as necessary.

If a specimen is removed from a store or display, fill out, sign and date a 'specimen removed' slip or comments label, and put this in its place. Keep unused slips safely to avoid misuse.

6.10 Loans out

You may be asked to lend specimens to an outside borrower, perhaps an academic researcher or a schoolteacher. Your museum may already have a general loans policy and procedure stating who can borrow, what kinds of objects can be borrowed, and what insurance arrangements should be made.

A good geological loans policy might include the following:

1 Loans to schools and colleges etc should not normally include material from the main collections, but should come from a separate collection of expendable 'school loan' material, if possible newly collected or bought. If you already have a school loans collection check its history, and if you can't be sure that it doesn't contain important material, stop lending it until the museum's geological collections have been curated. Many museums have important specimens in their school loans collections.

2 Loans of material from the main collection can be made for research, photography and other purposes so long as the borrower agrees to strict conditions.

Borrowers' intentions and identities should be confirmed – for example by insisting on a letter (not phonecall) on an institution's letterhead, with a check by letter or phonecall to the same address if necessary. If the borrower does not belong to a university or similar institution, he or she should obtain a reference from, for example, a geological curator. Students or other temporary research workers often borrow specimens for their research and in these cases the loans should be made to their supervisors, who must take full responsibility for the specimens should their students move on suddenly.

Specimens should be carefully packed and numbered and a full record made of every item lent, with a copy of the list signed by the borrower. The museum should use the MDA Entry and Exit Forms if it does not have its own.

Original labels should be kept by the museum where possible and photocopies supplied if necessary. The specimen's place in the collection should be marked with a comments slip signed by the curator.

Loans should be made for a fixed period, renewable under certain conditions, with the option that specimens can be instantly recalled by the museum.

Specimens must not be cast, peeled, cut into, sampled, altered, cleaned, conserved, coated for photography or otherwise prepared without prior permission (see 10.10). The museum must be given the results of any analysis. Seek a specialist geological curator's advice if necessary.

Photography or other reproduction, and publication, is forbidden without prior permission on each occasion. There is no such thing as copyright to a geological specimen but the museum does have the right to require an access fee. It is usual to waive these conditions for publication in non-profit journals.

Any publication must cite specimen number prefixed with the MDA code for the museum, and the museum's formal name. The museum must be sent a copy of the publication, or perhaps a full reference and extract if the specimen is mentioned only briefly in a long paper or book.

Use of a specimen in any display should include a credit to the museum somewhere nearby (on the label or, for example, on a side panel).

6.11 Finding out more about your collection

The scientific or historical value of a geological collection is largely determined by what is known about it (see 2.2). Few collections are fully researched and many important specimens await rediscovery. You don't need to be a geologist to produce useful results from collections research.

If you are lucky your collection will have primary information in the form of registers, catalogues, lists, indexes, early museum reports and old correspondence. Old labels may be of distinctive design, display particular styles of handwriting, or contain original collector's numbers. Even without these, there may be information about the origin of the collection, and some specimens may be individually identifiable, eg from published accounts.

Collections research has been greatly helped by several recent publications (see the Bibliography). Many of these specialist works are too expensive for most museums, so why not encourage your local Area Museum Service to include them in its library?

These books will provide references to obituaries, etc, which will themselves lead to original papers and other primary information. The *Proceedings* of the Geologists' Association and of the Geological Society (the latter often incorporated in the *Quarterly Journal of the Geological Society*) contain useful obituaries of members, as does the *Mineralogical Magazine*. The *Geological Magazine* is also useful. Local societies often publish membership lists and obituaries in their journals, and the local press may contain references to the activities of collectors and of the museum itself, often in considerable detail.

Old Geological Survey memoirs name important local collections and localities. Problems of geography, especially before local government reorganisation in 1974, can be solved with an inexpensive secondhand gazetteer (eg Bartholomew's Gazetteer pre-1970). Neighbouring and national museums may share the same collections and hold original documentation.

Local university and college libraries and the County Records Office may hold documents, and it is always worth checking your list of names against the library index. The local library and even the librarian's office files may contain older museum records, books, and old runs of journals, including rare or annotated items, especially if the museum and the library share a common origin.

The description of new material in the scientific literature (see 6.8) has always depended on the collections of amateurs and museums. Many but by no means all papers state the location of specimens and it is always worth checking through old papers about local geology, and the local society publications, especially those by the collectors of your museum's specimens. Remember that these papers may give a previous owner who is not mentioned in the museum's records. The *Proceedings* of the Geologists' Association, *Quarterly Journal of the Geological Society*, *Geological Magazine*, *Annals and Magazine of Natural History*, *Mineralogical Record*, and (for fossils) the *Monographs of the Palaeontographical Society*, all contain many references to material in museums and private collections. Another useful source is M G Bassett, 'Bibliography and index of catalogues of type, figured and cited fossils in museums in Britain', *Palaeontology* 18, 753–773, 1975.

Finally, remember *The Geological Curator* not only as a source of information but also as a valuable place to ask for help and publish the results of your work.

7 Storage

The aim of good storage is to protect and make accessible the museum's collections. The three main elements are location, furniture and specimen containers. The choice of one will usually depend on the others.

7.1 Location

Cellars and attics have long been favoured sites for the geology store but both are inappropriate as they can expose the collection to extremes of temperature and humidity, and damage from flooding or roof leakage. Choose a location where you will be able to maintain a relative humidity of around 50%. With very large collections, consider also the floor-loading capabilities of the store. As geological collections are mostly composed of specimens of relatively uniform size and weight, it is not difficult to estimate the total weight of your collection. Wherever possible avoid locations which involve climbing stairs, as this is particularly hazardous when carrying heavy or awkward specimens.

7.2 Furniture

A cabinet with flexible drawer spacing – the ideal

The best way to store most types of geological material is in drawered cabinets. These can be constructed of wood, plastic or metal. Choose wood throughout if you can (but not oak or birch, see 10.3), as this offers the greatest protection against humidity changes, vibration, abrasion and fire. Drawers should be close-fitting or glass-topped if your cabinets lack doors, but ideally doors should be fitted to maximise protection and exclude dust. If you are obtaining new cabinets choose a system which allows you to interchange the drawers and vary their spacing. A roller-racking system may be worth considering if space is limited, and may differ little in price from traditional systems (see *The Geological Curator*, vol 4, no 9).

Alternatively, shelves can be erected to hold acid-free cardboard boxes or heavy duty plastic bakers' trays with lids. Access depends on moving these containers so don't make them too heavy; for the same reason, don't store any geological material above head height.

7.3 Specimen containers

The best type of specimen container is a good quality acid-free card tray lined with white paper. Order sizes which tessellate to fit the drawers, with one tray for each specimen or group of specimens. A useful set of sizes is 2×3 ins, 3×4 ins, and 4×6 ins, or the nearest external dimensions of trays which will fit in your drawers. Put specimen labels in the base of the tray under a layer of acetate sheet. These containers have no lids and should only be used in dustproof storage. They are best used in drawered cabinets but can with care be used in lidded bakers' trays or cardboard boxes.

Lidded specimen containers are most useful where the cabinets do not offer sufficient protection from humidity changes and dust, or where the containers are to be put into larger boxes. Old glass-topped specimen boxes are excellent and should be saved. Modern plastic alternatives are cheap and are particularly useful for containing hazardous or humidity-sensitive specimens. Small cardboard boxes with card lids can also be used but are less than ideal as finding one specimen can mean opening hundreds of boxes. Clear but less rigid acetate lids fitted to card trays are a good and cheap alternative.

Specimen containers

Good quality self-sealing plastic bags are a useful and cheap way to store robust material, if no better alternative is available. These should be bought in a size that is as wide and deep as the box they are to go in. Put them in neat rows, not on top of one another, and not too many in one box.

Always use good quality acid-free storage materials as they work out cheaper in the long run. You should be able to get specimen containers locally – check with your local Area Museum Service.

7.4   Special considerations

Large objects should go on shelves or on a pallet, never directly on the floor, especially if this is concrete. This avoids damage from vibration and floor cleaning. Ideally these shelves should be inside a cupboard but if not then each specimen should be covered with polythene sheeting. Never pin this sheeting to fronts of storage units, but lay it over individual specimens. Smaller objects should be placed in boxes.

Very small specimens should be placed in stoppered plastic tubes or small lidded plastic boxes. Use Plastazote foam or acid-free tissue to stop them rolling around. Material mounted on microscope slides should be placed in purpose-built slide boxes or cabinets and kept in an environment identical to that of the larger fossils and minerals, that is, a relative humidity of around 50%.

Two things to avoid are most foam plastics and cotton wool. Foams disintegrate into a fine dust over a relatively short period. If you need to use foam, eg for storing Ice Age teeth and bones, only use a stable type such as

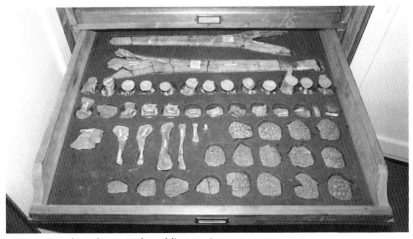

Plastazote can be used to protect large delicate specimens

Plastazote. The problem with cotton wool is that it becomes attached to small and delicate specimens. A modern alternative is non-fibrous cellulose wadding but even this is not without its problems. Most specimens need no more than a good quality specimen container such as a card tray.

7.5 Packing and transport

Geological specimens are heavy and can be brittle, so extra protection is needed when material is being moved. The basic methods are the same as for storage. Use acid-free tissue to wrap specimens. Prevent physical damage by using cellulose wadding, tissue paper, bubble pack or even newspaper (but don't let this contact specimens as it soils them easily). Use bags to prevent mixing or loss of documentation. Take special care with humidity-sensitive specimens, and minerals, which easily bruise and break. Get advice if you are considering the loan or transport of type, figured, rare, delicate or large items. Do not discount the possibility of sending such items with a courier.

8 Organising collections

It is relatively easy to put a geological collection in order as there are many good classification systems to help. There are no firm rules on which system to use but any indexes you create (see 6.6) should complement not duplicate this arrangement. Before you organise the collection ask yourself what you will most often want to find – a fossil of a certain type, fossils from particular beds, or material from a particular local collector? This will determine the subdivision of your collection.

Good examples of named collections should be kept intact

8.1 Whether to keep named collections intact

Named collections should not be integrated into the general collection if there is greater interest in the collector or in the collection as such than in the individual contents. Many geological collections are of historical interest (see 2.2, 3.2 and 6.11) and any good example, such as a 'cabinet' collection, should be kept intact. Objects in individual named collections should be left in the collector's original order. Put a note in each drawer saying 'in original order' and a plan of the arrangement in a history file. If not of interest in themselves, these collections can be integrated into the main geological collection but be doubly sure to record the name of the collector on every specimen's label and register entry (see 6.4). If this is done the collection can be reassembled when required.

8.2 The basic principles

Geological collections consist for the most part of fossils, minerals and rocks, and this may be adequate subdivision for a very small collection. The systems outlined here involve further subdivision into smaller groups. How far you take this depends on your collection's needs but as a general rule it may be worth subdividing again if your smallest grouping occupies more than one box or drawer.

There is no need to subdivide to the same level throughout, eg you may not need to go beyond 'Cambrian' for some of your collection, but need to subdivide 'Jurassic' much further, depending on the relative numbers in each category.

Leave plenty of space throughout for expansion and rearrangement – a minimum of 20%. Remember to allow space for material on loan or display. Put all material of the same type in number order so that new items are added to the end of a series.

It is best not to have a primary subdivision into local and non-local as this usually leads to the neglect of the latter. Type, figured and cited specimens, and valuable, hazardous or environmentally sensitive items, have special security and environmental requirements (see 6.8, 9, 10, 11, and 12). They may need to be stored separately.

8.3 Fossils

System 1

First subdivide by age (see appendix 2), then as far as necessary by biological category such as ammonite or plant (see appendix 3), alphabetically, or into local and non-local. Finally arrange specimens of the same type numerically. This is the most commonly used system.

Age	Fossil	Alphabetical	Number
Triassic	. . .	. . .	. . .
Jurassic	Ammonites	Dactylioceras	1978.221
		Harpoceras	1933.2
		Hildoceras	1986.44
		Psiloceras	1935.66
		Psiloceras	1935.67
	Brachiopods	. . .	. . .
Cretaceous	. . .	. . .	. . .

System 2

First subdivide by category of fossil (appendix 3), then as necessary as above. This is useful if you know little about geology and your collection is used mainly for simple comparison or display.

Fossil	Age	Alphabetical	Number
Gastropods	. . .	. . .	. . .
Ammonites	Triassic	. . .	. . .
	Jurassic	Arnioceras	1947.72
		Dactylioceras	1978.221
		Psiloceras	1935.66
		. . .	. . .

For a very small collection, no further subdivision is necessary:

Fossil	Number
Gastropods	. . .
Ammonites	1933.2
	1935.66
	. . .

8.4 Minerals

Appendix 7.1 gives a classification of minerals which can be used to organise your mineral collection. Appendix 7.2 gives a lexicon of mineral names and where they appear in this classification. It will also help to sort out the multitude of mineral synonyms.

There are many alternative systems which give numbers to each mineral species. The one most often found in museums is the Hey system which, for example, allocates quartz to 7.8.1. These classifications have the major shortcoming that they split up familiar structural groups such as garnets. The system given in appendix 7 aims to avoid this.

Where there are a large number of minerals of the same type, eg quartz, they can be further subdivided by locality or into provenanced and unprovenanced. If you have large suites of minerals from the same locality, keep them together; this is particularly important if your museum is in a mining area. Put all minerals in each final subdivision in number order.

Class	Mineral	Locality	Number
Molybdates	wulfenite	. . .	. . .
Silica	quartz	Britain	1919.7
	quartz	Britain	1919.21
	quartz	Italy	1847.34
	. . .	. . .	. . .

8.5 Rocks

Appendices 4, 5 and 6 give classifications and lexicons of common types of igneous, metamorphic and sedimentary rocks, which can be used to organise your collections. Again, if you have suites of material from particular localities, keep them together.

9 Storage and display environment

Humidity, temperature, light and atmospheric pollution all affect the long term stability of geological material (see section 10).

Storerooms should be dark and well insulated – not like this

9.1 Humidity

Much damage results from exposure of humidity-sensitive geological specimens to extreme or fluctuating humidities. Aim to maintain a steady relative
humidity (rh) between 45% and 55%, preferably at 50%. Problems will
develop if the rh is allowed to fall below 40% or exceed 60%. In a heated
store or gallery expect low humidities in winter and high humidities in
summer. In an unheated cellar levels may remain unacceptably high
throughout the year.

The best way to control humidity is with a humidifier and dehumidifier
linked to a humistat. Air conditioning systems seldom produce satisfactory
results and should not be relied on. Keep a check on humidity levels
throughout the year in every area where geological material is stored or
displayed, by using a recording thermohygrograph, which can be hired from
your Area Museum Service. It may work out cheaper however to buy your
own monitoring equipment, perhaps with an Area Museum Service grant.
An even cheaper alternative is to use a number of dial hygrometers, but
check these regularly as they are prone to error.

The effects of fluctuating humidities can be reduced if room and cabinet
doors are close fitting or carry gaskets, and windows are doubleglazed.
Raising or lowering the room temperature can help if the air is cool and
damp, or conversely warm and dry, but this should only be considered as an
emergency measure. A small number of especially sensitive specimens can
be protected using silica gel preconditioned to the correct rh but this method
is restricted because 20 kg (45 lb) of silica gel is needed to effectively buffer
one cubic metre (1.3 cu. yd) of air, and because of the need for regular
preconditioning. Even so, silica gel can be effective in sealed display cases
especially if room humidities do not vary dramatically from the optimum.
Polythene bags or sheeting can act as an effective short-term buffer against
fluctuating humidities so long as material is not placed in bags when wet or
in a damp atmosphere.

Some mineral specimens may require special conditions (see appendix
7.2).

9.2 Temperature

Temperature in itself is less critical and is unlikely to cause direct damage
provided extremes are avoided. However, relative humidity is directly
dependent on temperature and fluctuating temperatures, as caused by
heating being switched off at night, will also mean fluctuating humidities.
Localised heating or cooling due to the sun, tungsten lighting, waterpipes,
stone floors etc can also create harmful conditions.

9.3 Light

Glues, consolidants, labels and some minerals are adversely affected by exposure to light. Keep storage conditions dark. Place light-sensitive specimens in boxes to prevent accidental exposure (see appendix 7.2). Do not use original labels, correspondence, notebooks or prints in displays unless you can keep visible light and ultraviolet levels low (50 lux and 75 μWL^{-1}). Regularly change these items or make copies for display. Tungsten lighting is less damaging than daylight or fluorescent lighting, but it produces more heat and should not be installed within cases.

9.4 Atmospheric pollutants

These are of two kinds – particles and gases. In the still air of the museum store suspended particles are able to settle, coating everything in a fine dust which is usually only noticed when it has become a serious problem. This problem is reduced if the collection is stored in cupboards, boxes or even bags (section 7). Many minerals show chemical deterioration in a dirty atmosphere. Many minerals and fossils are difficult or impossible to clean.

Acetic acid and other vapours emanating from birch and oak cabinets, felt and some paints and glues can have a harmful effect on fossils (see 10.3) and tarnish or damage minerals. Tobacco smoke also damages geological collections.

Mineral collections can themselves be a source of pollutants which may be harmful to you (see section 12).

10 Conservation problems

Contrary to popular belief geological material is very susceptible to conservation problems. Inspect the collection at least twice a year and make sure you can spot problems. Take preventative measures and be sure that all work is done by a specialist geological conservator. *Remember that treated specimens continue to deteriorate if the cause of the original problem is not dealt with.*

Ask your Area Museum Service for help. If they don't provide a specialist geological conservation service, keep asking them until they do so. Don't try to do it yourself without advice from a specialist conservator.

This chapter outlines the common problems and what to do about them. Minerals are difficult or impossible to conserve once damaged, and most of the conservation techniques described here are not applicable to them (see 10.7).

Further reading: P R Crowther and C J Collins (eds), 'The conservation of geological collections', *The Geological Curator* vol 4, no 7, 1987.

10.1 Dust, dirt, and old varnish, glue, paint and plaster

All these have been added to the specimen, intentionally or otherwise, since it entered the museum. Their removal constitutes cleaning as opposed to the removal of 'dirt' or matrix attached to the specimen in the field: this last is preparation (see 10.10).

Symptoms Loss of detail and contrast between specimen and matrix; peeling of old varnish.

Cause Inappropriate storage or display conditions; old or inappropriate display and conservation techniques.

Prevention Dust problems can only be controlled by improving storage or by air conditioning. Never paint the matrix around a specimen. Do not allow inappropriate conservation techniques.

Treatment Superficial dust can be gently blown off or brushed off in an air extraction system (see 12.2). Washing is permissible with hard, insoluble rocks but it invariably causes a build-up of dirt in crevices and pores. Never wash minerals and do not even brush delicate minerals. Ingrained dirt, stains, and old varnish, glue, paint and plaster are a matter for a specialist geological conservator. The conservator will remove them from fossils with careful use of solvents, scalpels, an air abrasive or an ultrasonic cleaner. It may be impossible to clean a mineral without damaging it. The air abrasive is a miniature sandblaster, using a soft powder in an air jet. The ultrasonic cleaner uses high frequency sound in a tank of fluid to break the dirt off the specimen. Layers of plaster and concrete are removed with a hammer and chisel or an air-pen (a miniature 'road drill').

In the wrong hands cleaning can damage or destroy a specimen. Solvents can attack the specimen or its supporting consolidants, or fix the dirt more deeply. Air abrasives can easily remove the surface of a fossil and ultrasonic cleaners can remove the matrix or destroy the complete specimen.

10.2   Pyrite decay

Pyrite decay is a common problem in a wide range of fossils and minerals, especially in those from clays, coals, and pyritic nodules. If left unchecked it will lead to the total destruction of the specimen as well as its label and packaging.

Symptoms Yellow, white or grey powdery growth on the surface of the specimen; characteristic acrid sulphurous smell; moist litmus paper gives an acid reaction; packaging and labels have a brown, scorched look.

Cause The mineral pyrite oxidises in relative humidities above 60%, expanding to crack the specimen and releasing sulphuric acid which destroys labels etc. Pyrite occurs as large crystals or microscopically dispersed in clays, coals and nodules. Both types are susceptible to decay. Decay is not caused by bacteria, as was previously thought.

Prevention Maintain a relative humidity between 45% and 55% (see 9.1). Coating in plastic or varnish does not prevent decay.

Treatment Carefully brush or scrape away the decay products and put the specimen in an environment of lower relative humidity (but not too low: see 10.6). Place labels in a small polythene bag and put them with the specimen but not in direct contact. Send the affected object and labels to be conserved. If untreated, decay continues even at low humidities. The conservator will treat small, non-friable fossils by immersion in a solution of ethanolamine thioglycollate, and larger or friable ones in ammonia gas or vapour. Exposure to ammonia gas produces a rusty stain, and ethanolamine thioglycollate sometimes leaves a purple residue.

10.3 Salt efflorescence and Byne's Disease

Salt efflorescence can affect any specimen but it especially affects those collected from the seashore, particularly porous rocks like chalk. Byne's Disease is an unrelated efflorescence affecting calcareous (limy) fossils. Both can be confused with mould (10.5).

Symptoms White or colourless powdery, cubic or hairlike crystals on the surface of the specimen.

Cause Fluctuating humidity levels and the evaporation of moisture from the specimen cause the migration of salts to the outside of the specimen, destroying its surface detail or splitting it apart. Byne's Disease is caused by acetic acid vapours from storage or display materials (see 9.4).

Prevention Wash material from the coast unless it is friable or soluble (5.1, 10.6). Maintain a constant humidity. Avoid oak and birch cabinets.

Treatment Brush off surface deposits and place in an improved storage environment. Seek specialist advice if the problem persists.

10.4 Breakage, abrasion and bruising

This is one of the greatest causes of damage to geological specimens, which are brittle and easily fractured (see also 10.6).

Symptoms White scratches and bruises, chipped corners etc.

Mineral with chipped corners

Cause Bad storage: specimens touching each other, rubbing on bottoms of drawers above, or carrying the weight of overlying boxes; vibration; poor handling; separation of old glues such as shellac (reddish black) or fish glues.

Prevention Improve storage. Handle as little as possible, holding the specimen tray in preference to the specimen. Do not rely on old glued joints, especially when carrying specimens. Take care with minerals, which often have fine fibrous coatings.

Treatment Fossils can be glued together with HMG glue if needed for display. A broken fossil can show more information. HMG can easily be removed with acetone. Old glued joints need attention from a specialist. Do not use 'superglue' (cyanoacrylate), epoxy resin or water-soluble glues. Fillers should only be used by a specialist and where they support a joint. Bruises and scratches can sometimes be removed, but only by a specialist.

10.5 Mould

Mould can attack specimens, labels and packaging. It is easily confused with salt efflorescence (10.3).

Symptoms Foxing on labels and specimens (brown flecks and spots). Growth of white, black, brown or green hairlike strands.

Cause Relative humidity above 60%.

Prevention Reduce humidity.

Treatment Mould can be removed with the fungicide parmatol. Ensure that label inks are permanent. If the problem is extensive or persists, seek specialist advice.

Mould

53

10.6 Splitting specimens

This is most common in Ice Age (Pleistocene) teeth, tusks, and bones; shales (including those containing large ichthyosaurs or plant fossils); coal and wood.

Symptoms Distortion, developing cracks and eventual fragmentation.

Cause Low or fluctuating relative humidities; vibration.

Prevention Maintain a constant relative humidity around 50% (see 9.1).

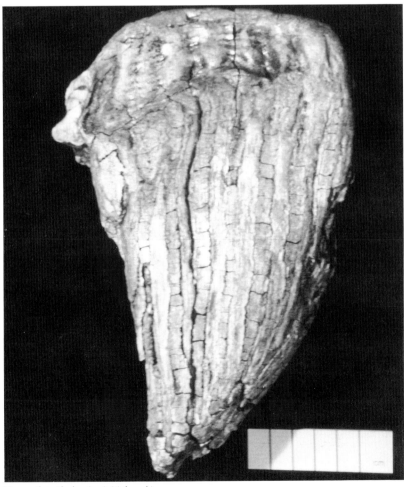

Mammoth tooth showing initial cracking

Treatment This should only be undertaken by a specialist geological conservator. Fossils are consolidated with solutions of various plastics. Don't be tempted to do it yourself: you could end up with a highly glossy specimen looking as if it is made of plastic. Consolidated specimens continue to deteriorate if the cause of the original problem is not dealt with.

10.7   Minerals: special problems

Many minerals preserve a delicate balance of physical and chemical characteristics which are easily destroyed or inadvertently falsified by inappropriate cleaning and conservation. Consequently techniques which are widely used in the treatment of fossils and archaeological specimens are rarely applied to minerals. Never do even the most minor repair, and in particular do not wash or polish specimens, but seek out a specialist conservator.

Some minerals are affected by light, humidity, temperature or vibration. The special requirements of various minerals are listed in appendix 7.2. The processes of decay and alteration are complex. They can be slow and subtle, and result in disintegration, colour change, shrinkage, cracking, powdering, or the formation of crusts and the growth of new minerals. If you suspect that damage is occurring see appendix 7.2 for possible causes. Create microclimates if necessary for particularly unstable minerals, using silica gel preconditioned to the right humidity.

10.8   Documentation: special problems

Specimen labels are as important as the specimens and can be more vulnerable. For example, silverfish can be particularly destructive, and pyrite

Silverfish damage

55

decay (10.2) and mould (10.5) can affect labels in conditions of high humidity. The specialist geological conservator will deal with labels but it may be worth sending important ones to a specialist paper conservator.

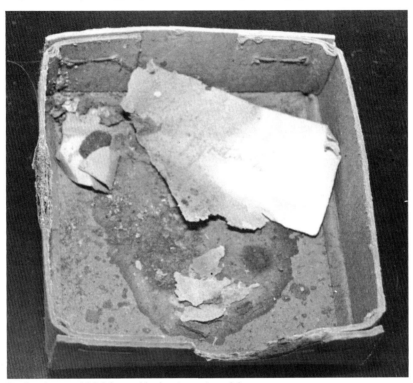

Cardboard tray and label damaged by decaying pyrite nodule

10.9   Getting material conserved

When conservation problems arise, seek out a specialist conservator. Don't be tempted to do it yourself: techniques have changed greatly in recent years and geological conservation is now seen as a specialist field. Your Area Museum Service or the GCG should be able to direct you to one of a growing body of people specialising in this field.

Before material is conserved, ask the conservator what he or she intends to do. The conservator is there to advise and help you, but it is your responsibility to decide whether the work should be done, and to point out the important characteristics of the specimen: for example, do you keep its fine Victorian mounting?

When items are returned after treatment record the details of the work in your documentation system, and file the records and photographs supplied by the conservator in a history file. Make a reference to the work on the specimen label, on its back if necessary. If you have not dealt with the original cause of the problem, then even newly conserved material will continue to deteriorate.

10.10 Preparation and research techniques

Occasionally a researcher may want to undertake work (including the making of replicas) using material in your collection which may result in the alteration or even total destruction of some specimens. If you receive such a request, first obtain, in writing, full details of the techniques to be used, the probable effect on the specimen, and the use to which the results are to be put. Do the level of the research and the possible value of the results warrant the effect on the specimen? Is there a risk that the specimen might produce no useful results? Could a non-destructive technique be used instead? If in doubt get advice from an expert, eg from the British Museum (Natural History), especially if type or figured material is involved.

Obtain references if necessary and check that the person undertaking the actual work is competent. Ensure that the work is fully documented and photographed, and that copies of the results and of any resulting publications are given to the museum. If the specimen is likely to be totally destroyed then treat it as a disposal (see section 13), and if it is a fossil consider having a cast made. Samples of matrix should be kept if it will otherwise be totally removed.

You may also want to have a specimen in the collection prepared for display. The preparation of minerals is problematical. Mineral specimens may consist of a single species but often contain an assemblage of species as well as the host rock. The use of preparation techniques to remove coatings or expose crystals may destroy part of this assemblage and hence the scientific value of the specimen. There are few occasions when this is desirable.

Listed below are some of the most commonly used techniques in research and preparation, usually used only on fossils. With the exception of photography, these techniques are for experienced hands only as most are in some way irreversibly destructive. Before allowing them to be used, find out in what ways they are likely to damage or alter the specimen.

Mechanical preparation or development Removal of the matrix surrounding a specimen using hammer and cold chisel, pins, scalpels, electric engraving tools, pneumatic engravers (air pens), high frequency sound (ultrasonic

Specimen being mechanically prepared

cleaners and probes), or an air abrasive (a miniature air jet with abrasive powder). If done properly these leave the fossil undamaged.

Chemical preparation or development Removal of the matrix using acids, protecting and supporting the fossil with a coat of plastic.

Embedding Setting a specimen in a block of plastic; only acceptable on rare occasions.

Moulds and casts Using rubbers, resins, plasters, etc, to produce an exact replica.

Thin sections A piece is cut and glued to a microscope slide to be ground down until it is transparent and can be viewed through a microscope.

Scanning electron microscopy (SEM) Tiny samples or whole specimens of small objects are fixed to stubs and sometimes coated with special compounds before being photographed at high magnifications.

Cutting and polishing The polished surface can show hidden detail. It is sometimes done by a stonemason under contract.

Peels The specimen is cut and polished, then the surface is etched with acid and an impression is taken with acetate sheet.

Serial sectioning A specimen is slowly ground down and peels taken every so often till a complete series of sections has been taken.

X-raying and CAT-scanning The specimen is photographed in two or three dimensions with X-rays. This can be very useful as it is non-destructive.

Staining Limestones and other rocks are occasionally dyed to distinguish between similar minerals.

Microfossil extraction The collection of tiny fossils using chemicals to break up the rock.

Photography Aim to get even illumination with a slight highlight from the upper right as published. Avoid great contrasts of light and shade. Fossils (not minerals) are sometimes slightly wetted or even immersed in various liquids, or they can be coated in substances such as ammonium chloride. If this is to be done be sure that you are told beforehand and that the liquids or coatings are not harmful and can be removed.

Dating Various methods are used in geology to measure the age of specimens from the relative abundance of isotopes. In museums, this usually concerns the carbon dating of Ice Age (Pleistocene) bones, shells or plants. Depending on the richness of the material and the technique used, the sample size needed ranges from 300 grams to a very small amount. This material must be uncontaminated, that is, without consolidant.

Perfect casts of ammonites

Ichthyosaur paddle before and after cleaning

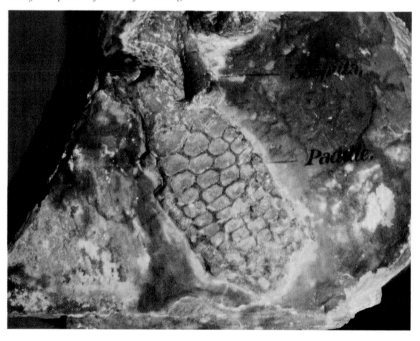

60

Pyrite decay

White salt efflorescence

61

11 Security

11.1 Fire, flood and intruders

Geological collections and their documentation are as valuable, fragile and susceptible to damp, dirt, fire, flood, vandalism and theft as any other collection. Too many geological collections are kept in a museum's worst and least secure storage: easily opened display cases, wet outhouses, poorly locked rooms, attics with leaky roofs and damp, easily flooded cellars.

The museum must satisfy certain basic standards of care and protection for its collections, including geology, for it to qualify for Area Museum Service funding under the Museum Registration scheme. However, it should also be possible to obtain grants to reach these standards. Check with your Area Museum Service (appendix 9).

11.2 Theft by visitors

One of the most difficult forms of theft to combat is that by the official visitor who is there to see and handle the collections in store. At particular risk are mineral and fossil collections, especially but not only rare minerals, meteorites, and gemstones. The only way to cope with this is by taking reasonable precautions which the honest visitor will understand and approve.

Have the entire collection curated, recorded and documented, with copies of records in a secure place away from the store. You cannot discover or prove theft if you do not know what you hold and where it is kept. A photographic record of at least the most important specimens is very useful for this and other purposes. If your only records are MDA Cards or Extension Sheets, or similar looseleaf systems, then make sure that the visitor does not have access to them, as it is easy to remove all record of a specimen.

As an absolute rule, allow no visitor access to the collection unless he or she has previously written to you and you have been able to reply to a definite address. The visitor must either belong to a reputable institution or give a personal reference from a geological curator or an officer of a reputable amateur society, such as the Geologists' Association or the Russell Society (for minerals). If you are in any doubt, follow up the reference given, as some thieves have used bogus letters.

Supervise the visitor. If this is not possible, do not permit access: thieves have a habit of turning up unexpectedly in order to evade supervision.

If possible, bring the specimens the visitor wants to see to a workroom or office for examination. If a visit to the store is unavoidable, for example to check for specimens possibly misidentified and so placed in the 'wrong' drawers, open only one cupboard at a time, and lock it afterwards.

Instruct your staff never to allow visitors into the collections without warning or supervision, even if their faces seem familiar.

Be particularly wary of repeat visits and always maintain the same security measures.

Never accept visitors' offers to buy or exchange 'duplicate' or 'inferior' specimens in your collection: you don't know how valuable they really are. Apart from the problems implicit in any disposal of specimens (section 13), this is a common form of theft.

If in any doubt, or if a possible theft has occurred, contact a specialist geological curator or a GCG committee member (see 3.1). They may know of someone's previous activities.

If your precautions fail and you suffer theft, remember that you will have a hard time proving it in court if your records are not adequate.

A stolen MDA Card could remove all record of a specimen

Fossils recently stolen from a museum by a collector

11.3 Staff

Unfortunately it is the case that the museum's own workers, including volunteers, have the best chances of theft and of altering the records (if any) to conceal it. Most are honest but a few carry out a rather uncomfortable proportion of museum thefts. Again, seek written references from a specialist geological curator or a reputable amateur society. Be careful if you employ active collectors and dealers. Apart from the security risk, their personal interests may clash with those of the museum.

11.4 Valuation and insurance

Geological specimens are worth money. You will probably be surprised at how much! Many a small museum has an ichthyosaur skeleton worth up to £15,000. Smaller and more portable specimens can be worth several hundreds or even thousands of pounds. Precious and semiprecious stones, and rare minerals, not only gold nuggets, are obvious risks. If you insure your collections at all you should have your geological collection valued. Remember the cost of the work you put into curating and storing it. It can be hard to find a specialist valuer but the GCG may be able to help (see 3.1).

12 Hazards

Geological material sometimes poses safety problems. It can be heavy, poisonous or radioactive.

12.1 Physical hazards

A lot of geological material is, quite simply, heavy. If you have heavy specimens you should have some way of moving them safely when needed. It is a great help to keep them on a pallet and to move the pallet plus load, rather than the object on its own. This also minimises damage to the object. If you have more than a few heavy items you will need special storage facilities such as heavy duty racking, ramps, and trolleys. You may need these for heavy items in other collections, such as sculpture or Roman mosaics. Avoid stairs if possible. The ramps will also help staff and visitors who have difficulty in walking, and those with wheelchairs and prams.

12.2 Dust and chemical hazards

Some minerals are hazardous because they are poisonous or otherwise harmful. They include some of the most toxic substances known. You should therefore assume that they are all toxic if inhaled or swallowed. Minerals which are also toxic on skin contact are listed in appendix 7.2. You will minimise the hazards if you follow a few basic ground-rules:

- Most intact minerals are, on the whole, safe (but note that native mercury gives off toxic vapour, and see 12.3 for radioactive minerals).
- All mineral dust, including clay or quartz dust, is harmful if inhaled. Problems can arise if the minerals are breaking up and spreading dust. Keep such specimens in covered, sealable containers such as plastic boxes or sealed bags.
- Fibrous asbestos minerals and processed asbestos should also be kept in sealed containers.
- Do not drink, eat or smoke in the store or workroom.
- Don't lick specimens – they may not be rock salt!

- Use warning labels, if possible the international standard signs (available as stickers and on reels of tape), for known toxic minerals.
- Do not leave toxic or unidentified minerals where others (especially babies and children) can handle them. Toxic specimens such as galena are unsuitable for school loans sets and any 'feelie' exhibitions.
- Treat unidentified minerals with care, whether found in the museum or brought in by the public. Inquiry specimens can include dangerous artificial substances such as industrial waste or explosives.
- You will normally have little to worry about if your collection is in secure and clean storage, you wear overalls and if necessary disposable gloves, and you always wash your hands thoroughly after handling minerals. Wear dust masks in dusty areas, especially when cleaning up a dirty store.

12.3   Radioactivity

Many museum collections contain radioactive minerals, usually uranium and (less commonly) thorium minerals (see appendix 7.2). There are three main hazards:
- direct radiation from the specimen
- swallowing or breathing in radioactive dust from specimens which are breaking up
- the accumulation of the radioactive gas radon which is slowly emitted by these minerals.

Some radioactive minerals such as torbernite and autunite are not normally intensely radioactive. Store and handle them as described for toxic minerals (see 12.2), handle them as little as possible, and keep them in a ventilated area away from workrooms, offices and public areas. Use the standard radioactivity hazard symbol on the cupboard and the specimen boxes, and try not to breathe the air in the newly opened cupboard. Half a

Hazard warning stickers

dozen small specimens then present a negligible risk if handled only very rarely, say one hour a year.

However, other radioactive minerals such as uraninite, pitchblende and other uranium oxides are much more hazardous, and advice should be sought on their storage or removal to another institution with special radioactive storage areas. University collections in particular may have such specimens.

If your museum has radioactive minerals it may well come under the regulations for the storage of radioactive materials. Consult a local health and safety officer, or a radiological safety officer in a local university or hospital. See Brunton, Besterman and Cooper, *op cit.*

13 Transferring or destroying geological material

Transfer is the permanent movement of material from one museum to another. Disposal is movement from one use to a potentially destructive one, such as school loans, or actual destruction. Transfer is, of course, a form of disposal. Geological collections have in the past been particularly prone to ill-considered transfer and disposal, perhaps because of a widespread failure to comprehend their importance.

Disposal is not in itself unethical but it is when undertaken:

* for the wrong reasons
* without legal right
* by unqualified personnel
* using incorrect methods
* without consultation, publicity or record

Your museum should already have a policy on disposal to guide the curator and the trustee. Why are you thinking of disposing of geological material? Disposal should be positive, a part of putting specimens to their best possible use, for example:

* to provide material for school loan
* to reveal new scientific information
* to effect better curation (eg in another museum)
* to ensure better use

Less acceptable reasons are:

* to make space available
* to aid expansion in other disciplines
* because conservation problems appear incurable
* because specimens seem to fail to meet modern documentation standards
* because material is non-local
* to raise funds

Are the problems you perceive real, or might they disappear with research and specialist advice? Have you had the collection examined by a geological curator (see 4.1)?

Whatever the reasons they will have to meet the approval of colleagues. Consultation is an essential element in the disposal process. Firstly, seek the advice of a geological curator. He or she may call in subject specialists to help make a full assessment. At the same time gather together all known records relating to the collection – registers, labels, letters, reports, publications and so on. Check how the museum came to possess the material as this affects the legal position (see Brunton, Besterman and Cooper, *op cit*, and various authors, 'The disposal of museum collections', *Museums Journal*, 87, 119–139, 1987). For example, if a specimen has been given to a public or charitable museum (that is, it is in trust), collected by a staff member or otherwise collected, bought or improved with public funds, including research grants, then it will have to go to another public institution or charity. Make sure there were no conditions attached to its acquisition, such as 'no disposal'.

Next consider possible new 'owners' and the method of disposal – by gift, sale or loan. Recipients should always be educational, non-profitmaking institutions, never private individuals: this is most ethical and minimises legal problems. Specimens are rarely totally useless and dumping is usually unacceptable. The method of disposal and perhaps the receiving institution may be determined by the legal situation, especially if matters are referred to the Charity Commissioners. Any funds raised should be reinvested in the museum.

Finally, decide how much work needs to be done on the collection before transfer can take place. Few collections are in a perfect state of documentation or organisation, and disposal can destroy evidence of a collection's history (see 5.2).

Prepare and present a report to the trustees. If they approve it, publicise the proposed transfer in the *Museums Bulletin*, *The Geological Curator* and the *Biology Curators' Group Newsletter* before it actually takes place, allowing plenty of time for publication and representation. Your specialist advisor may also recommend a note in certain academic circulars.

As a result of this process you will probably have a far clearer understanding of the importance and potential of your geological collection. You may in fact decide that it should stay where it is. If it is to be moved, some basic curation will be needed beforehand. Send copies of all records with the collection to its new home. The disposal must be fully documented: compile a file for your museum containing copies of all reports, correspondence, lists and photographs. Report this disposal in the journals above as appropriate, and certainly to the GCG Recorder (see 3.1).

If as a result of collections research you discover past disposals then pass the information to the GCG Recorder so that future workers know that material has been removed and perhaps where to find it.

Using collections

14 Introduction: deciding what to say

Before you start using your collection, decide what you are going to say with it. This applies to displays, lectures, publications, guided tours and even what you sell in the museum shop.

Your museum is the local museum and your first aim should be to concentrate on the local geology. There may be no other museum to do this. Avoid the common mistake of trying to approach geology from a general point of view, for example the classification of rocks, however easy it is to copy from a textbook. This is of relatively little interest to local people compared to 'their' rocks and 'their' scenery. Instead, find out about your own area. This may take more work but is far more worthwhile. If you don't know anything or don't have time to find out about the local geology, get someone to write a simple account for you. This can be a good job for someone without curatorial training.

Get some idea of what is interesting about local geology. How does it relate to people's everyday life? Geology controls scenery, including topography, rivers, animal and plant life, and human settlement, industry and transport patterns. Don't forget quarrying, mining and oil drilling. Are there any rocks, fossils or minerals which are interesting in their own right? For example, have any good dinosaur skeletons been found locally, or is your town the result of the exploitation of a special mineral or a spa? Does the history of local geological research – which may well include your own museum – contain any interesting stories?

What sort of people come to the museum, and what might they want if you improved your geological service? (Remember that the present demand may be deceptively small precisely because you have little or no geological service.) At the very least, local people and visitors will bring their finds in to be identified. A display of common local finds is useful, especially if you show typical finds (often broken and worn) alongside more complete (and often more understandable) but much rarer specimens. If many educational field parties visit your area then they will want a more technical display and a selection of somewhat more advanced books on sale, especially local guides.

What resources do you have or what can you easily get? First, of course, look at your collection and your museum library. What are their strengths? Next, is there anything useful in your industrial history, archaeology and art collections, such as mining tools, Roman lead ingots and jet necklaces?

Then see what other museums or organisations, including visitor interpretation centres, NSGSD Geological Locality Record Centres, and national and local societies, cover the geology of your local area. What do they do?

What are their displays like? Do they produce any useful publications which you could sell? Can they give you help and information? Could you borrow particular specimens to complete your displays? Try not to duplicate their displays and services unnecessarily, especially if they are close by. Your Area Museum Service or County Consultative Committee (if you have one) may be helpful here.

15 Different approaches

There are different ways of looking at geology, and it is often possible to use your own specialist knowledge and skills to interpret the subject. Here are some ideas: obviously, some may not apply to your area.

If you find that your local geology or collections allow you to take more than one approach then do so. You might, for example, have one display about local geology and a second display about the history of local research. Or you may have an unusual specimen which warrants a separate display in its own right.

15.1 The geological approach

This is the most obvious approach, looking at the local geology as geology.

What was the geological history of your area? The earth is thousands of millions of years old, but your local rocks will represent a far from complete record of a small fraction of this age, rather like a history book which only contains William the Conqueror and Queen Elizabeth II.

First find out about the structural geology and geomorphology to establish an overall chronology: what are the local rocks and how do they lie? Which rocks were formed during each period? How was this pattern formed? Is it one of layers of younger sedimentary rocks laid down on top of older ones? Or did volcanic rocks burst up through fissures to penetrate and overlay the older rocks? How have the rocks been tilted and then eroded to give today's scenery? Was this erosion done by the sea, or by glaciers and their meltwaters during the Ice Age?

Then look more closely at each main period. Don't feel obliged to use the geologists' terms such as 'Precambrian' and 'Oxford Clay' as your names. 'The volcanoes of Charnwood' and 'Sea monsters of Milton Keynes' will mean far more to the average visitor, but don't forget to mention the ages and geological periods in the smaller print.

What happened in each period, and how was each kind of rock deposited? Can this be explained clearly and simply? Don't assume that the visitor has any specialist knowledge.

It is impossible to describe local geology adequately from text and specimens alone. Photographs, drawings, maps and models are essential. Illustrations of similar modern environments are very useful for subjects such as desert sandstone with wind-faceted pebbles. Wherever possible, redraw geological maps in a simplified form and show the major landmarks. You could put them on a three-dimensional model of the local scenery, which can be cut in two to show the underlying strata.

You can also treat in more detail a specific topic such as cave systems or the range and beauty of the local minerals.

Finally, the past and present work of museums in local geology may also be worth a display.

It can be difficult to find good colour photos of a particular subject, such as a volcano or crocodile. Cutting them out of books and magazines is not a good idea as the colour inks used are not permanent enough for prolonged exposure to light. Photographing them is better. Displaying a single copy of a photograph is not in itself an infringement of copyright, but making the copy without permission probably is (see 20.3). You can have a permanent print made from a colour transparency from a commercial picture library on payment of a reproduction fee. The rates are not cheap but the photos are usually excellent and the library may give a discount if you explain what you want it for. Alternatively you can try your local geological society, university geology or zoology departments, and the Geological Museum and British Geological Survey (addresses in appendix 9).

A landscape doesn't need to be dramatic to be of geological interest

15.2   The biological approach

A good way of displaying fossils can be to treat them as living animals. Look at them just as you would today's local wildlife. Take a fossil such as a clam, sea urchin or squidlike belemnite. How did the animal move, and what did it eat? What was its environment like – the open sea, or a sandy seabottom? Did it move or was it fixed, and if so to what – a log or rocks? How does its shape reflect its lifestyle?

How did these animals fit into the ecology of the period? What ate what? Do you have enough fossils of one period to represent the ecosystem as a whole? (See especially McKerrow, *The ecology of fossils*.) Do your fossils truly reflect a past ecosystem, or is the record biased by the lack of softbodied animals such as worms, and by the drifting of dead animals from 'alien' environments? Dinosaurs are often found in rocks laid down under the sea, not because they were seagoing animals, but because their corpses floated down rivers into the sea.

Can you find specimens or photographs of living animals related to your fossils, to give some idea of how they looked in life?

Are your local fossils difficult to recognise as fossils? This can be because the fossils are strangely preserved, or because they do not look like the more common types of animal or plant. This can confuse people and may need explanation.

If you work in a small local museum it is not usually wise to try and cover palaeontology as a whole. In particular, you will have little opportunity to discuss evolution and extinction beyond the basic fact that these cause the differences between fossil and modern animals.

Life in colder times

15.3 The historical approach

Look at the history of research into local geology. There may be some very interesting stories there, especially about the people involved. Were there any famous geologists or great local discoveries? Your own museum, if it is old enough, may have played a part. Was it founded as a result of interest in local geology? What historically interesting specimens do you have in your collections? Do you have any relevant paintings, manuscripts, or nineteenth century books with fine lithographs?

Also, think about the exploitation of your local rocks. What rocks and minerals were quarried and when? What were they used for? Stone was used for buildings, roads, and manufacturing. Bricks were made almost everywhere. What materials were used in your local buildings, and why? Were building materials imported or exported? What effect did the canals and railways have on this? Were local materials supplanted by imported brick and slate? Many old quarries have been completely obliterated and their past existence comes as a complete surprise to many people. Earlier cultures may have used local stone for the manufacture of tools and querns.

Hugh Miller – 19th century Scottish geologist

Geology became a practical science through the work of canal and railway engineers, whose tunnels and cuttings provided much information and sometimes specimens. Are there any links with people such as Brunel or famous excavations like Edgehill Cutting and Box Tunnel?

Local quarry and mine operators can be very helpful in providing information and specimens, and perhaps letting you see their archives and old photographs. Early Memoirs of the Geological Survey and information from your local Geological Locality Record Centre (see appendix 1) may also contain much of relevance. (See also 6.11.)

15.4 Geology and art

Landscape artists and 'atmospheric' painters instinctively record the product of geological activity, while many sculptors use the composition of stone to reflect their ideas. The displays at the Ruskin Museum, Coniston, show the particular influence of geology and other natural objects in the paintings of the Pre-Raphaelites. Geological lithographs are themselves an art form; works such as Agassiz' *Recherches sur les Poissons Fossiles* fetch high prices not for the text but for the beautifully reproduced drawings. As in Romantic landscape paintings, geological features often appear as evocative backdrops to outdoor action on film. Local geologists of fact and fiction may become the subjects of books and films such as *The Voyage of the Beagle* and *The French Lieutenant's Woman*.

The decorative arts undoubtedly owe much to geology. It provides raw material such as marble, gemstones and clays for jewellery, decorative inlays and ornamental *objets d'art*. Displays linking these naturally occurring materials and the finished article can be both informative and attractive. For instance, a whole series of displays can be created about pottery, ranging from the earthy constituents of the clay to the mineral sources of the colours used in glazes (see P Rado, *An introduction to the technology of pottery*, Pergamon Press, 1966).

Museum specimens are an especial source of inspiration. Wedgwood's own geological collection inspired his early jasper and agate wares. Today's students often use the patterns and textures of rocks, minerals and fossils to create new designs for anything from pottery to fabric. Others explore the challenge of capturing them in drawing or painting.

The ornamental use of stone in buildings and manufacture has existed from the earliest times. Each area has its own range of building stones and clays for bricks, as well as importing a variety of decorative rocks (see section 21).

Agateware teapot

16 Some display techniques

16.1 Mounting specimens

When mounting specimens from the collections for display, always consider their fragility, rarity and significance within the collection. Do not mutilate them, or use glues which cannot be removed. Do not put specimens where the public can touch them unless they are securely fixed and specifically intended for this purpose; discuss your plans with a specialist curator first, and if possible collect fresh specimens for the purpose. Minerals are not useful in touchable displays; they are too brittle and may be poisonous (see 12).

Horizontal surfaces

These present few problems as most geological objects have sufficient weight to prevent movement. Narrow shelves should be slightly inclined backward or have a lip or other means of preventing specimens from jumping off, as even traffic vibration has been known to cause this. Many materials can form effective backgrounds for geological exhibits, from glass, stone or painted wood to satin, velvet or cork. Hessian has become rather dated, and felt can emit harmful vapours.

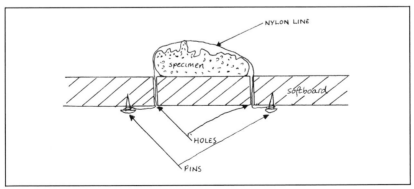

Securing a specimen to a softboard base using nylon line

Inclined surfaces

Softboard is the most flexible material for supporting objects on inclined surfaces. It is easily cut and drilled. Objects can be secured with nylon

79

fishing line attached to the reverse side of the board with drawing pins or staples. Alternatively, push fine stainless steel pins through and snip off their heads for an invisible support. For more delicate specimens cover the pins with plastic tubing, perhaps stripped from electrical cable. Heavier specimens can be supported on blockboard using a strip of timber screwed to the baseboard. Large rocks – but only those collected specifically for the purpose – can be fixed to a baseboard using bolts glued into holes drilled in the back of the rock. An epoxy resin can be used for a permanent joint, with fibreglass used to fill around the bolts if needed. Other glues and resins can be used. Epoxy and polyester resins are difficult or impossible to remove. Don't use them on fossils or minerals.

Vertical surfaces

Adopt the techniques above or make special perspex or fibreglass mounts. Gluing specimens to walls, or setting them in plaster or concrete as 'open' displays, are drastic measures and you should first seek advice from a geological curator.

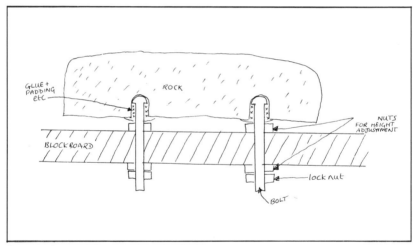

Securing a large specimen with bolts on a blockboard base

16.2 Modelling in polystyrene and plaster

This method can be used to create lifesize models of extinct animals or to reconstruct the missing parts of bones. Your local taxidermist may be able to suggest other techniques.

1 Get as many illustrations as possible from various angles of the animal you want to reconstruct. Decide whether to make a complete reconstruction or just a half-relief model. Choose a scale; if you use the

model to interpret a fossil, it is best to make the model a full-size replica.

2 Take a block of fire retardant expanded polystyrene. If necessary, glue and joint together smaller blocks with wooden dowels and plaster or expanded polystyrene glue. Do not use ordinary polystyrene cement.

3 Draw the side view of the animal on the block, either freehand or by squaring up a tracing of the illustration.

4 Cut around the outline with a hacksaw blade or heated polystyrene cutter. Use the heated cutter in a well-ventilated area.

5 Continue to shape the model by eye. Ignore detail at this stage. If you cut too much off, it can be filled with plaster. Aim for a slightly undersize finished shape. Now consider how to mount it, and insert the necessary dowels or wires.

6 Mix up small amounts of dental plaster (or other quicksetting plaster) and apply to the surface. Cover the whole body. Build up eyes and other details. If the plaster is too thick, it can be removed by softening with water and scraping with a scalpel.

7 Finally, paint and varnish the specimen.

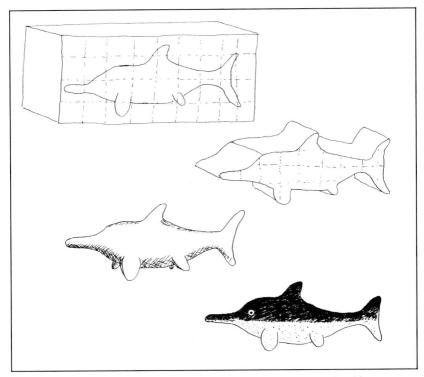

Top to bottom: marking the outline; initial cutting; final shaping, and the finished model

81

17 Resource centres

There is a limit to what, or how much, you can say with a display. The visitor who wants to find out more may not know where to look, or be able to obtain the references. A resource centre or study corner may offer the answer. Essentially a collection of books and maps, it provides a flexible reference for the visitor to answer his or her own queries, and find out more.

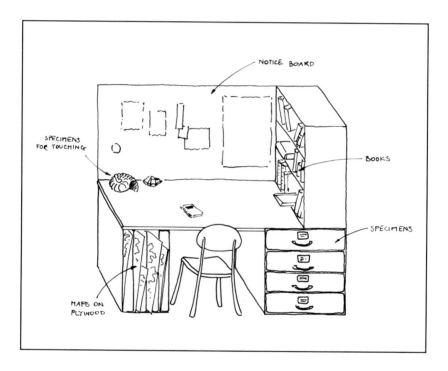

17.1 Location and furniture

The centre should be set up in the gallery as it is important that it is linked to the displays. Any space will do but natural light is preferable – a window space is ideal (but make sure that the light is not harming nearby displays). The only furniture needed is a table or worktop, some shelving, and one or more chairs.

17.2 Content

It is up to you what you put in the centre and there is no reason why it shouldn't cover other subject areas displayed in the gallery, such as natural history or archaeology. Here are some geological suggestions:

Books and articles Choose ones which are particularly relevant to the displays and to local geology (see the Bibliography). Always include a copy of the local memoir or memoirs of the British Geological Survey, and also their Regional Guide. The Geologists' Association may have produced a local guide, and their *Proceedings* will almost certainly contain reports of field trips in your area. Local societies and museums will also have produced articles and booklets on local geology. Do not overlook old books as they contain much of interest. You can also add general books on the identification of fossils, minerals and rocks, and a geological dictionary. Old and irreplaceable books, and articles from old journals, should be photocopied (but see below). You can even compile your own books: a scrapbook of articles and press cuttings; a do it yourself identification guide for common local fossils, using photocopies from various old monographs; a photograph album of local sections, landforms and building stones (but don't use original prints here); and information on the museum's own collection and local sites from the local Geological Locality Record Centre.

Maps Get maps showing the local geology, topography, land use and soils. These can be glued or laminated onto plywood boards and slotted into a storage space under the worktop.

Specimens Local fossils, minerals and rocks can be stored and displayed in secure glass-topped drawers, perhaps with accompanying notes; make sure that they are not damaged by drawers being banged open and shut. It can be a good idea to have a box of relatively common, easily replaceable specimens for people to handle; similar criteria to school loans apply when choosing them (section 19).

Noticeboard Display news of local and national finds, research, local societies, lectures, field trips and press cuttings. Local and quality national newspapers and the *New Scientist* will provide more than enough material. This gives the gallery a lively, up to date feel, but don't leave things up too long or you will get the reverse effect.

Books are expensive but shops and individuals may be willing to provide certain items with the donor acknowledged on the inside cover. Authors may have spare reprints of articles. Never include valuable or irreplaceable items. Photocopying can help, especially for books and articles out of copyright (50 years after the author's death, or after publication, whichever is later). The law on photocopying copyright books and articles without permission is complex (see 20.3, and the *Copyright, Designs and Patents Act 1988*).

Photocopies obtained through a public library, or photocopies of public library books, may only be used for private research and study, and thus cannot be used in a resource centre. These restrictions do not apply if you have permission.

Setting up and maintaining a resource centre is an ideal job for a volunteer, although centres can be designed for low maintenance.

Normal museum security should help to prevent material from disappearing, especially if visitors' bags are controlled. Books and other items can be made too awkward to remove by being placed in large folders.

One final point: make sure the centre doesn't look like a staff work area. Signs such as 'Natural Science Centre' or 'Feel free to browse' may help. Good examples of centres can be seen at Warwickshire Museum and, on a much larger scale, at Liverpool Museum.

18 Geological enquiries

When it comes to dealing with geological enquiries, it is particularly important to know your own limits. It is wrong to believe that as a curator you should know everything! If you find you can't provide the information required then exploit local expertise or refer the enquirers to another museum. Alternatively you could provide them with the books and reference specimens to make their own identification.

Most enquirers only want relatively simple information, for example that the stone they brought in really is a fossil ammonite, it is X million years old, and something on how it lived and how it came to be where it was found. If particular types of enquiry are common then it may be worth producing information sheets, perhaps with local help. Possible subjects are 'concretions', 'ammonites', 'fossils from the Chalk', 'local minerals', 'pebbles from the seaside', and so on. Check whether the 'Thumbs up' scheme provides a relevant leaflet.

A few basic books on fossils, minerals and rocks, and local geology, are essential. If you are not going to use them yourself, they may still help an enquirer. Well-organised and accessible collections will also help you to identify enquiries.

If you can't deal with an enquiry on the spot use your own enquiry form or the MDA Entry Forms (see 6.3). These ensure that the necessary details about the collector and specimen are recorded. The form you use should be ready-printed so that the enquirer understands that the museum's advice is an opinion only; not to be used for commercial purposes; valuations are not given; and the specimen can be disposed of if not collected within a fixed period.

Enquiries are a ready source of new acquisitions but it is important to ensure that they meet the museum's acquisition criteria, particularly as regards documentation (see 5.1).

Further reading: T Sharpe and W D I Rolfe, 'Geological enquiries', *Museums Journal* 79 (2), 61-62, 1979.

19 Education

Museums with geological collections and expertise can provide a range of valuable educational services to schools, adult education groups and the general public. The scope of these services will depend on the museum's resources and on the various customers' needs. You may be able to leave the more specialised services, such as fieldwork, to a nearby large museum.

The basic resources needed are the collections of specimens and information. To develop their use properly needs some geological expertise and an understanding of the educational system. Obviously it is essential to select the most appropriate specimens and information for the job.

Displays are the most obvious educational resource, and the most useful displays are often the simplest. They should be based on a selection of good specimens, chosen to illustrate a clear theme with brief labels and good illustrations. Displays become more useful when supplemented by a range of publications, including free leaflets, inexpensive booklets and various worksheets. Teachers and group leaders also appreciate an advice sheet with details of the museum's facilities and resources.

Some museums will have a room which can be used by visiting groups. This may contain specimens suitable for handling, and equipment for illustrated talks by museum staff or group leaders away from the distractions always present in display rooms. The same resources can be used with infant school groups or adult extramural courses. The room can also be used for local society lectures, museum Saturday clubs, children's holiday activities, public lectures and so on.

Loans of specimens are welcomed by many teachers and evening class tutors. Loan services range from shoeboxes of specimens wrapped in newspaper that are chosen and taken away by teachers, to custom-built packs delivered by van. In all cases the specimens must be good quality, typical examples which can stand up to inexpert handling and are of no scientific value. See section 6.10 for how to select material for school loans; the same criteria apply to material kept in the museum for handling. Remember that some minerals, including common ones such as galena, are toxic and should only be used with care (section 12).

Fieldwork provides educational opportunities which complement those available in museums as rocks, fossils and minerals can be seen in their natural context rather than in an artificial environment (see sections 21, 22 and 23.3). Museum staff may be available to lead groups and provide information about sites. Teachers, tutors, field trip secretaries and the general public appreciate publications which help them to visit sites. However, the sites must be carefully chosen to suit different groups, ranging from infant schools to Open University students. All must be safe, access-ible, have a range of useful features and be able to withstand visitors without risking their scientific value. For these reasons, you should consult your local Geological Locality Record Centre (see 3.1) and the Nature Conservancy Council before publishing any such guides.

It is very useful to liaise with all the various organisations concerned with education in your area. The Local Education Authority (LEA) is a means of communicating with schools, while their advisors and teacher-centre wardens can also help to advertise your resources. It is also useful to contact the Association of Teachers in Geology and the Association of Science Education. Evening class tutors can be contacted through the LEA, the Workers' Educational Association and the local university's Extramural Department. The Nature Conservancy Council, the National Scheme for Geological Site Documentation (see 3.1) and the local County Trust for Nature Conservation will be able to help with the selection and development of sites for geological fieldwork. The Group for Education in Museums can advise on the general development of your museum's educational service (see appendix 9 for addresses).

20 Producing geological guides

The preparation of geological guides and leaflets is relatively simple and is within the capabilities of many local museums and societies.

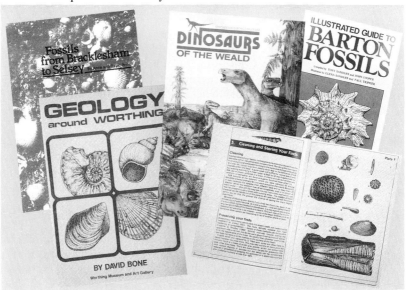

20.1 Decide what you want your guide to do

Guides and leaflets can satisfy a variety of possible needs. See what gaps need filling – it is a good idea to provide information which your visitors regularly ask for. Then check what else is available locally and regionally, including the 'Thumbs Up' scheme (3.1).

Guides have three possible functions, each of which can be backed up with a museum display:

- To identify and describe local finds, in order to assist your enquiry service.
- To give background information on local geology, including rock types, ages, and outcrops, fossils and minerals, and perhaps a list of sites worth visiting.

- To discuss specific topics, such as important geological sites or collections, local building stones, and the influence of geology on the landscape and on man's activities, such as brickmaking, quarrying and farming.

Remember that any reference to specific sites will encourage visitors, and avoid sites on private land unless permission has first been obtained. Discuss sites with local bodies (see 3.1 and 19). Scientifically important sites such as Sites of Special Scientific Interest are best avoided unless it is made quite clear that hammering or collecting are not allowed. Emphasise that cliffs, quarries and mines, working or abandoned, are dangerous. Avoid encouraging visits to working mines and quarries.

20.2   Finding an author

Don't feel you have to write the leaflet yourself – you can find a willing author. Get help from your local geological society or a geology or geography teacher at a local college or school (try the Association of Teachers in Geology). Geological curators and other local museums which have produced similar guides may be able to help.

Whoever writes the guide, be sure to clarify certain points first:

- At what level of reader are you aiming – the older child or the intelligent layman? It is particularly important not to pitch the level too high for the audience – and sales – you are aiming at. Think like a good journalist: remember vocabulary, sentence length, and the complexity of the concepts involved. Don't use jargon, and explain even the simplest of geological terms used.

- Decide on the length of text and the number and type of illustrations such as maps, sections, line drawings and photographs of fossils and sites. You may need to get quotations from some printers at this stage to ensure you can afford what you have in mind.

- Work out a schedule with dates for the first draft, illustrations, designer's deadline etc. This helps ensure that the work gets done in a reasonable time and doesn't drag on, especially if you are mounting an associated exhibition or hoping to catch the tourist season. Allow enough time for proof-reading and corrections by yourself and the author.

- Sort out any payments, royalties or copyright. Generally, if you are commissioning someone to do the work then it is your copyright, not theirs, and it can certainly be made a condition of a contract that copyright rests with the commissioning body.

20.3 Sources of illustrations

Geological specimens are notoriously hard to draw or photograph except by expensive professional methods. You can try searching for line drawings and engravings of the items you want. Books out of copyright (normally 50 years after the author's death or after publication, whichever is later) are especially useful as there is not the usual need to get permission or pay reproduction fees. However, the law on copyright illustrations is complex and you should check C H Gibbs-Smith, 'Copyright law concerning works of art, photographs and the written and spoken word', *Museums Information Sheet* (Museums Association), and the *Copyright, Designs and Patents Act 1988*. Get good copies made by a photographer or by the bromide process (ask your designer or printer about this). However, don't rely on the names or identifications in the older books as many will be wrong or out of date. Also check the accuracy of drawings.

20.4 Bibliography and glossary

A bibliography is useful on two counts. It enables the interested reader to delve further into the subject – you may set future geologists on their way – and it also shows that you have referred to specialist works for the content of your publication. However, don't include items for their own sake if they are not useful to the reader.

Any publication intended for readers who are not familiar with the subject should have a glossary. This need not be very long but should contain simple explanations for the more technical words used.

20.5 Production and costs

As before, you need a logical approach to get the best results.
1 Decide what money you have available for the production. Can this be increased? (See 4.4) If you go for outside help you will first need to have a good idea of how many copies you are producing.
2 Decide if you are going to use a graphic designer. This can make a lot of difference to the publication's appearance and save many sticky fingers and telephone calls to printers. Ask other museums which designers they have used, either freelance or in-house (can you buy some of their time?). Ask to see samples of the designers' work and get quotes (not estimates) from them.

3 Decide on the print run. The more you print the cheaper each is, but your money will be tied up for a longer time, although they could be purchased as goods for resale. Ask other museums how well similar publications are selling, and remember that you will sell many more of a publication associated with an exhibition. Good publicity and display of the publication will also help sales.

4 Get quotes from a printer. The printer will show you paper samples as this considerably affects the price. Then decide on how many colours of ink you want. You may be able to restrict multicolour effects to just the cover and the pages with maps. Now ask for quotations for at least two different print runs. You will probably be surprised at the difference in cost.

21 Geology in the high street: building stones

Buildings are a permanent exhibition of a surprising variety of local and exotic stones which are readily seen during a shopping trip or on the way to work. A guidebook which explains their use and history can enhance the public's appreciation of this heritage.

The high street gives easy access to local rocks as well as to those which cannot otherwise be studied without travelling long distances. Sometimes the local rocks are from quarries which no longer exist. The urban 'outcrops' are in many cases much fresher than natural exposures, and sometimes highly polished. They include igneous, metamorphic and sedimentary rocks from as far away as Scandinavia, the Alps, the Mediterranean, Africa, America and India, as well as from the British Isles. They can be of considerable educational value, complementing rock collections housed in museums, schools and colleges. The way in which improved transport links and changes in building techniques have affected the choice of materials will be of interest to students of local history, industrial archaeology and architecture.

The type of guidebook produced will depend on the range of building stones visible locally, the effort put into research and the target readership. It can be a short pamphlet of general interest, a comprehensive educational geological guide discussing (for example) the mineralogical differences between various rocks, or an analysis of building stones within local architectural and industrial history.

Building stone can be identified from its lithology (that is, type of rock such as sandstone or limestone), perhaps with the help of local geologists, or by its provenance (that is, where it came from).

A good first step is to walk town trails in neighbouring areas where similar guides have been published. This will give some idea of the commoner building and ornamental stones, such as larvikite, Portland Stone, Yorkstone, Shap granite, Peterhead granite, Lake District slate and others found in most cities. The variety of approaches adopted by the different guidebooks may suggest the most suitable for your needs. A list of guides for various parts of Britain is obtainable from the Education Officer at the Geological Museum.

Some of the most interesting building and ornamental stones are used as cladding on modern buildings and shopfronts. These stones are widely distributed and careful comparison with stones in other towns and cities using published guides can be enlightening. Alternatively they could be compared with the large collections held by the Geological Museum, the University of Cambridge and various importing companies.

While some stones are unique and highly distinctive, others are hard to identify visually, and more research is needed. If you confine your enquiries to a few specific questions, then property owners, architects, builders, shopfitters and planning authorities are often keen to help.

Local companies who quarry, import or distribute natural stone can be very helpful and may even provide a few samples. Stone companies are listed in the *Natural Stone Directory* (Stone Industries, Park Lane Publications Ltd, 70 Chiswick High Road, London W4).

Many building stones used in older buildings and cemeteries are no longer quarried and their identification may need a different approach and considerable research. The materials used in the more important buildings may be recorded in local archives, in old newspapers or in historical accounts, which often specify the quarries. The *London Illustrated News* gave details of stone used in many buildings throughout the UK. Geological maps and memoirs, and old town and topographic maps, show locations of old quarries, some of which may still be visited to study the rocks. Older Geological Survey memoirs, in particular, often mention the actual product of old quarries. The older maps and memoirs can be found in some public libraries, universities and at the British Geological Survey.

Small booklets describing churches, civic buildings and large houses and castles can be quite helpful. These buildings are typically of local stone with imported stone used for ornamental interior work, such as pillars and plaques of Scottish granite, Connemara marble, Italian marble, alabaster, and Caen stone brought in from further afield. These are usually different from the exotic stones used nowadays, due to changes in importing patterns.

Older gravestones are often of local materials, now no longer quarried, while the Victorians preferred Scottish and Scandinavian granites. The origins of some of these granites may prove impossible to determine but their compositions and textures can still be described. The dates on gravestones and plaques record the changing fashions in stones used.

Caution is sometimes needed. Some rocks, such as the serpentinites or 'green marbles', are very similar in appearance even though from widely separate areas. Establishing their provenance needs considerable expertise and may not be possible. Wherever possible, trace the origins of a stone via architects' plans, fitters and importers, as this is the most reliable method despite the considerable patience needed. Even such painstaking research is not without problems. Rock names used in industry are, confusingly, not synonymous with geological usage. In general, the stone industry refers to most hard rocks as 'granite' and all softer ornamental rocks as 'marble', regardless of composition and origin. Some companies invent trade names for their wares and may adopt an existing name for a new, different import. In some cases, however, importers know the quarry locations abroad, and a study of the geological literature of that area can be valuable.

The most meticulous researcher will still be unable to locate the provenance of all the building stones investigated, but this should not detract from the guidebook's lively, descriptive and explanatory text. Rather than exhaustively listing the names of stones in the high street, use the rocks to illustrate basic geological principles. Volcanic ashes, cleavage, bedding, and aspects of metamorphism, igneous petrography, sedimentology and palaeontology are all well within the scope of amateurs, school pupils and college students when superb examples are so accessible. The guidebook can ask questions such as which sandstone blocks are upsidedown? are the fossils in the position they adopted in life? why is one building far more weathered than the other? and so on.

The Bibliography gives an introduction to the literature on building and ornamental stones. Use this, together with local archive work, and help from experts in nearby colleges, universities and museums, as the start for your own town trail.

22 Guided walks

Guided walks are a natural extension of a museum's activities, and geology is, of course, particularly suited to outdoor interpretation. They offer opportunities for active participation and firsthand experience of the materials and processes of geology.

The three essential elements of successful guided walks are:

* accessible and interesting sites
* enthusiastic and competent leaders
* widespread publicity

22.1 Selecting a site

It is probably easiest to arrange to meet at or near the site, rather than get involved in the cost and complications of organising coach travel, so the first requirement is good car parking nearby. It may be necessary to signpost the route to the meeting place. Ideally, the site should allow a circular walk, taking in several localities of interest, starting and finishing at the meeting place. If the main objective is interpretation, rather than walking, then the distance covered in an afternoon or morning walk will be fairly short, probably no more than a couple of miles. If the walk can offer some fossil or mineral collecting, this will be particularly interesting for children. However, responsible collecting is the aim, from sites not vulnerable to damage. Participants should be made familiar with the 'Thumbs Up' leaflet (see 3.1) and the *Code for geological fieldwork* leaflet published by the Geologists' Association, and be encouraged to collect only a few specimens from loose spoil. Such collecting also provides an opportunity to put forward a conservation message.

Safety is another important consideration and dangerous sites should be avoided. Any site, however, presents some risks. The party must be warned of possible dangers such as mine entrances, shafts, unstable slopes, loose rocks, standing water etc, in order to provide some measure of protection for the leader from claims of negligence. The advertisement or programme should also point out that visitors take part at their own risk. Disclaimers can be issued to indemnify the leader to a limited extent. However, like indemnity forms (which should be signed when access is permitted to, for example, a working quarry), these cover only claims against damage to property and not personal injury. It is obviously an advantage if the leader has some knowledge of first aid and carries a first-aid kit.

22.2 Selecting a leader

Leaders must be enthusiastic about their subject and keen to pass on their knowledge. They must be familiar with the sites and be prepared to check out the intended route and localities prior to leading the walks. A multidisciplinary walk is often well-received, so a leader who knows a bit about local history or natural history as well as geology is useful. Alternatively, several leaders of varying specialisms can offer more authoritative opinions and comment. They must be able to explain clearly and simply, as most members of the audience are unlikely to have any experience of geology and its jargon. It is useful to have a brief leaflet available for distribution, explaining the geology of the site or illustrating, for example, the kinds of fossils to be found there. Participants can read this at their leisure and remind themselves of what was seen on the walk.

As the walks are largely family activities, the level of interpretation and walking pace should be suitable for children.

The leader should be prepared to change plans at short notice and have arranged some alternative route or activity in case of inclement weather. The Institution of Geologists' *Code of practice for geological visits to quarries, mines and caves* should be followed and permission sought before entering any private property (see appendix 9 for address).

22.3 Publicising the walks

If a series of walks or activities is planned, a leaflet, which can also be used as a poster, with details of each walk should be prepared and distributed to local libraries, museums, tourist information offices, societies etc, as well as to the participants of each walk, as they usually ask about the next one. The leaflet should include details of the meeting place with National Grid Reference, date and time; the need for strong footwear and waterproof clothing; and an indication of what is involved in each walk.

When selecting dates for the walks, the dates of local events such as fairs or shows should be avoided if possible, as should major events such as Wimbledon finals. Saturday and Sunday afternoons seem to be the times preferred by participants, although midweek evening walks can also be well attended.

Newspaper advertisements should be placed a few days before each walk, and are probably the most effective advertising medium. It is often possible to obtain editorial cover, via a press release and a couple of photographs, or by inviting a reporter along on a walk. Guided walks offer good photo-opportunities which are usually of interest to the local press.

22.4 Attendances

Unless an advance booking system is operated, the leader will have no idea of the number of people to expect on a walk, and this can make route-planning difficult. It should, however, present no great problem. Requiring telephone or written bookings is an unnecessary administrative burden and unless a restriction in number is essential, booking is best avoided.

Attendances will vary depending on a large number of factors such as the extent of the advertising, the weather several hours before the start of the walk, the site itself (whether it is in a remote area, or near a large conurbation) and on other alternative attractions.

22.5 Costs

Costs fall into two main categories: leaders' expenses and advertising. Leaders' costs may involve fees or subsistence and travel expenses. Advertising costs are likely to take up 70% of the budget for the walks. One way of reducing costs would be to arrange the walks in conjunction with other organisations such as the National Trust, National Trust for Scotland,

and the National Parks authorities, and share advertising costs (addresses in appendix 9).

22.6   Structuring the walks

Each walk should begin with a brief introductory talk to explain what is planned and how long it will take. Frequent brief stops are better at retaining the interest of the group then fewer, longer stops. However, this will depend on the terrain as it may be possible to stop only once where there is sufficient space for the party to gather together. If the party is strung out along a narrow path, communication is difficult.

At the end of the walk, the leader should summarise simply what has been seen and remind the participants of the date of the next walk. The Bibliography gives some further reading.

23 Rock and Fossil Festivals

Collecting rocks and fossils is a popular hobby for children and adults alike. Local museums are in a prime position to encourage this interest and channel it into lively learning. This important role of popularising the subject can be done through permanent or temporary exhibitions, and by organising events for the whole family.

Here are suggestions for three types of event. You may like to have one or all of them in a Rock and Fossil Festival. Choose a good date, during the school holidays but not clashing with the Cup Final or Wimbledon!

A prerequisite of any event is, of course, good publicity. Distribute attractive and informative posters and handbills widely, particularly to local schools. Send well-written press releases to newspaper offices, local tele-

vision and radio stations, and freelance photographers and reporters. Can the museum shop stock up on geological items such as plastic model dinosaurs, badges and stickers? (See appendix 8.)

23.1 Identification day

This can be called 'The Rock 'n' Fossil Roadshow', and admission should be free.

Get a panel of three or four geologists from nearby museums, geological societies, colleges or universities to identify rocks, fossils and minerals. The panel should also include an archaeologist to deal with worked flints, pottery, etc, and a natural historian for bones, teeth and shells. Be sure that reference books will be available to confirm and illustrate the identifications. Also have a hand lens or microscope, weak acid and streak plates to aid identification. Supply plenty of pens and paper for the experts to write down their comments, and sticky paper dots to number items. Remind the experts that not everything brought in will be local.

Keep a table clear for items left for further identification or donation to the museum, and have enquiry forms, entry forms and transfer of title forms ready (see 6.3). Try to keep a count of the numbers of items identified and the number of enquirers.

Have available free leaflets on common fossils, rocks and minerals, and give each enquirer a 'Thumb's Up' leaflet (see 3.1). Produce a booklist for those who want to learn more about their finds. A local bookshop should be invited to come and sell books as the public usually show great interest. The local geological society may like to set up a table to display its activities and recruit new members.

Invite the media along and note any surprising or unusual items which may interest them. Finally remember regular refreshments for the panel.

23.2 Workshops

Why not invite a local geologist to advise and participate in the workshop?

Choose a topic such as ammonites, woolly mammoths or crystals, and prepare a temporary display of suitable material. If the geologist comes from another museum, he or she may be able to bring additional material. Write, or get someone to write, an information sheet and a booklist of further reading to distribute to participants.

Set a minimal admission fee to cover the cost of materials and decide on payment: by booking with a ticket, or at the door. Tell people on your posters or tickets whether to bring an apron, painting clothes, or a bag to carry their work home. Recruit adults to help and supervise each practical activity.

The geologist should give a short talk at the beginning of the workshop, followed by a question and answer session. He or she will probably want a slide projector and perhaps an overhead projector.

You can then run one or more of the following activities. If you do more than one, arrange them in separate work areas and let the participants move freely between each when they have done their pieces of work. Each activity could be run as a competition, with the geologist as judge, and prizes, perhaps donated by the local bookshop. Display visual examples such as posters, books and models to inspire production. Templates may also help. Be sure that everyone marks their completed work with their name and takes it home.

Model making Any of the following materials are ideal: cardboard, clay, plasticene, playdough, plaster, wire, pipe cleaners, papier mache, bubble

wrap etc. Self-hardening clay is best but if it is too expensive then ordinary clay will do, without firing, if handled carefully.

Making badges Borrow a machine from, for example, a local community arts centre, or just provide templates in different shapes to make up with card, fabric, paint and safety pins.

Fabric collage This is mainly for older children, making textured pictures with pieces of material which they choose, cut out and glue onto paper. Collect plenty of cloth and wool of different colours and textures in advance, from friends and colleagues. You may need to buy felt and 'fur' if you are not given enough. Provide thick paper of at least A3 size. You can also use objects such as pasta, string, wool, straw, shells, gravel and milk bottle tops.

Painting Freestyle painting on your topic. Outline pictures may help the younger children.

Depending on the activity you will need equipment and materials such as clay cutter, scissors, paint, knives, brushes, white glue (Polyvinylacetate), glue pots and applicators, pipe cleaners, card, safety pins, sticky tape, pencils, pens and paper.

23.3 Collecting trips for children

Sections 19 and 22 discuss the organisation of field trips. The following notes will help when organising a family collecting trip.

Choose a nearby site where fossils, rocks or minerals are common and easily spotted in loose pieces of rock. Check on access, parking (especially for coaches), safety, insurance and permission to visit and collect from loose heaps. Invite a local geologist to advise and lead. Prepare free information sheets describing the site, the nature and age of its rocks and common finds.

Bookings are essential. Arrange transport to and from the site. Ban the use of hammers or other tools (except by the geologist) and tell participants to bring a strong bag and newspaper to wrap finds, strong footwear, water-proofs (whatever the forecast) and food and drink if necessary. Invite enough parents and adults to ensure a good adult-to-child ratio and adequate supervision.

You need not spend more than 90 minutes at the site but your trip as a whole can easily last half a day. Take a first-aid kit, and a bucket and cloth in case a child is sick during the journey. If you have very large numbers with you then it may be helpful to put a numbered sticker on each child to help organise seating and supervision on and off coaches.

Bibliography

Books, maps and journals for reference and resale

Museum matters

T Ambrose, *New museums: a start-up guide*, HMSO 1987

C H C Brunton, T P Besterman & J A Cooper (eds), *Guidelines for the curation of geological materials*, Geological Society Miscellaneous Paper 17, 1985

P Doughty, *The state and status of geology in UK museums*, Geological Society Miscellaneous Paper 13, 1981

C Paine, *The Local Museum: notes for amateur curators*, 2nd edn, AMSSEE, 1986

Children and young people

There is a wide and changing range. Try the British Museum (Natural History), Dinosaur Books (Althea), Grisewood and Dempsey, Kingfisher, Ladybird, Piccolo, Puffin and Usborne. Many of the other books listed are also suitable for children, especially the dinosaur books. One of the many good books is: M Bramwell, *The nature trail book of rocks and fossils*, Usborne, 1983. The 'Know the Game' book *Collecting fossils* is sold by the Palaeontographical Society at a special cheap rate to museums.

General readers

General

D V Ager, *Introducing geology*, Faber and Faber, 1975

J W Barnes, *Basic geological mapping*, Geological Society Handbook, Open University Press, 1981

M J Bradshaw, *A New Geology*, Hodder and Stoughton, 1973

R Croucher and A R Woolley, *Fossils, minerals and rocks: their collection and preservation*, British Museum (Natural History)/Cambridge University Press, 1982 (Practical advice.)

Geological Curators' Group, 'Thumbs Up' leaflets

T R Owen, *Teach yourself geology*, 1983

A E Trueman *Geology and scenery of England and Wales*, Penguin, 1972 (Describes very effectively the interrelationships of geology, landscape and the manmade environment.)

D G A Whitten and J R V Brooks *The Penguin dictionary of physical geography*, Penguin, 1972

D G A Whitten and J R V Brooks *The Penguin dictionary of geology*, Penguin, 1972 (Inexpensive – will answer many questions on the subject.)

J B Whittow, *Geology and scenery in Ireland*, Penguin, 1975

J B Whittow, *Geology and scenery in Scotland*, Penguin, 1979

David and Charles publish a very useful series, *Geology explained in . . .*, explaining to the layman the geology of several areas, eg W Dreghorn, *Geology explained in the Severn Vale and Cotswolds.*

The social and intellectual history of geology

D E Allen, *The naturalist in Britain*, Allen Lane/Penguin, 1976 (Scholarly account of the social history of natural science.)

L Barber *The heyday of natural history 1820–1870*, Doubleday, 1980 (Racy, full of personalities.)

H Wendt, *Before the flood*, Paladin, 1970 (About the history of palaeontology, rather out of date but a convenient introduction.)

Identification (simple)

British Museum (Natural History) *British Palaeozoic fossils*, 4th edn, 1975; *British Mesozoic fossils*, 6th edn, 1983 and *British Caenozoic fossils*, 5th edn, 1975 (Well illustrated.)

W R Hamilton, A R Woolley and A C Bishop, *The Country Life guide to minerals, rocks and fossils*, Country Life (Also published as *The Hamlyn guide to minerals, rocks and fossils* – a good but necessarily short guide to common specimens found worldwide.)

Fossils

M J Benton, *Pocket book of dinosaurs*, Kingfisher Books, 1987

M J Benton, *The story of life on earth*, Kingfisher Books, 1986 (Useful as it covers plants and invertebrates – ammonites, sponges, etc – not just dinosaurs.)

R L Carroll, *Vertebrate paleontology and evolution*, Freeman, 1987 (Advanced review of fossil vertebrates, and the only up to date review of everything from fish to man.)

A J Charig, *A new look at the dinosaurs*, Heinemann/British Museum (Natural History), 1979

E N K Clarkson, *Invertebrate palaeontology and evolution*, 2nd edn, Allen and Unwin, 1986 (Quite advanced for the general reader but full of information about fossil animals and especially useful for biologists.)

M Collinson *Fossil plants of the London Clay*, Palaeontological Association Field Guides to Fossils No 1, 1983

I W Cornwall, *Bones for the archaeologist*, Dent, 1974 (Very useful for identifying many enquiries.)

R Fortey, *Fossils: the key to the past*, Heinemann/British Museum (Natural History), 1982 (Again, covers plants and invertebrates as well.)

L B and J Halstead, *Dinosaurs*, Blandford, 1981

W S McKerrow, *The ecology of fossils*, Duckworth, 1978 (An excellent reference, particularly useful for its block drawings of ancient ecosystems, and an accessible source of information on the lifestyles of particular fossil animals and plants.)

Monographs of the Palaeontographical Society (A specialist reference for the identification of fossils.)

J W Murray, *Atlas of invertebrate macrofossils*, Longmans/Palaeontological Association, 1985 (An advanced classification and identification guide.)

D B Norman, *The illustrated encyclopaedia of dinosaurs*, Salamander, 1986 (The most up to date and arguably the best dinosaur book.)

E F Owen and A B Smith (eds), *Fossils of the Chalk*, Palaeontological Association Field Guides to Fossils No 2, 1987

R J G Savage and M R Long, *Mammal evolution: an illustrated guide*, British Museum (Natural History), 1986 (An excellent and up to date review.)

E Schmid, *Atlas of animal bones*, Elsevier, 1972 (Modern animals such as horse and sheep, especially useful for enquiries.)

A J Stuart, *Pleistocene mammals of the British Isles*, Longman, 1982 (Important reference to British Ice Age finds.)

A J Sutcliffe, *On the track of Ice Age mammals*, British Museum (Natural History), 1985 (A good popular introduction.)

Treatise of Invertebrate Palaeontology (Definitive reference to invertebrate fossils.)

Rocks and minerals

Most museums will not need more than one general encyclopaedia of minerals and one modern listing of minerals such as Hey or Fleischer.

C Cipriani, *The Macdonald encyclopaedia of precious stones*, Macdonald, 1986 (Useful and informative introduction to gems and gemmology.)

E S Dana, *The system of mineralogy of James Dwight Dana*, 6th edn, Wiley, (Standard reference, first published in 1892, giving detailed descriptions of all minerals then known. Still very useful.)

W A Deer, R A Howie and J Zussman, *An introduction to the rock-forming minerals*, Longman, 1983 (Advanced text with valuable reference lists.)

D E Evans, *Investigating minerals*, National Museum of Wales, 1972 (An excellent elementary introduction.)

D E Evans, *Investigating and identifying rocks*, National Museum of Wales, 1977 (Useful elementary pamphlet.)

M Fleischer, *Glossary of mineral species*, 5th edn, Mineralogical Record, Tucson, Arizona, 1987 (Invaluable checklist of all current mineral species.)

N Fry, *The field description of metamorphic rocks*, Geological Society Handbook, Open University Press, 1984 (Fairly advanced.)

R P Greg and W G Lettsom, *Manual of the mineralogy of Great Britain and Ireland*, 1858. Facsimile reprint with supplementary lists of minerals to 1977 by L J Spencer and P G Embrey, Lapidary Publications, Broadstairs, Kent. (Properties and occurrences of minerals; very dated, but useful for checking localities of old collections. See also supplementary lists in the *Mineralogical Magazine* vol 42, 169–177; vol 47, 99–105 (Scotland); vol 52, 121–124 (Wales), and vol 52, 267–274 (Ireland).)

F H Hatch, A K Wells and M K Wells, *Petrology of the igneous rocks*, 13th edn, Murby, 1981

M H Hey, *An index of mineral species and varieties*, 2nd edn, 1962; *An appendix . . .*, 1963, and *A second appendix . . .*, 1974, British Museum (Natural History) (Absolutely invaluable, gives a chemical listing, a cross-referenced alphabetic listing of species, varieties and synonyms, and a dictionary of pronunciation.)

J Kouřimský, *The illustrated encyclopaedia of minerals and rocks*, Octopus, 1977 (A good basic introduction, including the history of their use.)

A Mottana, R G Crespi and G Liborio, *The Macdonald encyclopaedia of rocks and minerals*, Macdonald, 1983 (Good introduction to mineralogy with details and illustrations of common species. Excellent handbook.)

M O'Donoghue, *The encyclopaedia of minerals and gemstones*, Orbis, 1976

R Thorpe and G Brown, *The field description of metamorphic rocks*, Geological Society Handbook, Open University Press, 1985 (Fairly advanced.)

M Tucker, *The field description of sedimentary rocks*, Geological Society Handbook, Open University Press, 1982 (Fairly advanced.)

C Woodward and R Harding, *Gemstones*, British Museum (Natural History), 1987 (Well-illustrated elementary introduction to gemstones.)

A R Woolley (ed), *The illustrated encyclopaedia of the mineral kingdom*, Hamlyn, 1978 (Informative, readable and well-illustrated introduction to all aspects of minerals, including formation, properties, use, collection and curation.)

Collections research

G D R Bridson *et al*, *Natural history manuscript resources in the British Isles*, Mansell, 1980 (If the collection had associated manuscripts.)

J M Chalmers-Hunt, *Natural history auctions 1700–1972*, Sotheby Parke Bernet, 1976 (If the collection was sold at auction.)

R J Cleevely, *World palaeontological collections*, British Museum (Natural History)/Mansell, 1983 (Lists many known fossil collections.)

P S Doughty, 'Research: geological collections', in J M A Thompson (ed), *The manual of curatorship*, Museums Association and Butterworths, 1984 (A how-to-do-it guide.)

W A S Sarjeant (ed), *Geologists and the history of geology*, Macmillan/ Krieger (later volumes), 1980 onwards (A seven-volume series.)

C D Sherborn, *Where is the – collection?*, Cambridge University Press, 1940 (Largely superseded by Cleevely, though not restricted to fossil collections.)

H S Torrens, 'Locating and identifying collections of palaeontological material', *Newsletter of the Geological Curators' Group* (now *The Geological Curator*), vol 1, no 1, pp 12–17, 1974

Also check back issues of *The Geological Curator*, both the 'Lost and Found' section (index to vols 1–3 in vol 4, issue 2) and the journal as a whole.

Buildings and ornamental stones

M J Branney *The building and ornamental stones of Stoke-on-Trent*, Staffordshire Geological Recording Scheme Publication 1, 1983, available from Stoke-on-Trent City Museum (see references therein.)

A Consiglio, *A technical guide to the rational use of marble*, Italian Marble Industry, 1972

M H Grant, *The marbles and granites of the world*, 1955

J E Robinson, *London illustrated geological walks*, Books 1 and 2, The Geologists' Association, 1985 (see references therein)

J Watson, *British and foreign marbles*, Cambridge University Press, 1916

Interpretation and outdoors

G Binks, *Guided walks*, Countryside Commission Advisory Series no 4, 1978

R K Grater, *The interpreter's handbook*, Southwest Parks and Monuments Association, USA, 1976

P H Risk, 'Conducted activities', in G W Sharpe (ed), *Interpreting the environment*, pp 141–158, Wiley, 1976

T Sharpe and S R Howe, 'Family expeditions – the museum outdoors', *Museums Journal*, 82(3), pp 143–7, 1982

Booklets

Consider selling a selection of the cheap illustrated booklets published by the following museums (get their current catalogues, and check what nearby museums publish).

British Museum (Natural History) (Post: Sales Manager, Natural History Museum, Publications Sales, Freepost, London SW7 5BR).

Claws and *Archaeopteryx: the feathers fly*

Geological Museum (post: as British Museum (Natural History) above) *Britain before man* (describes a changing Britain in the vastness of geological time); *The age of the Earth* (how geological time is actually measured); *The story of the Earth* (describes the moving continents and other processes that have shaped the planet); *Volcanoes*; *Earthquakes*; *Moon, Mars and meteorites* (published by HMSO); *British fossils* (published by HMSO); *Gemstones*; *The geological map* and *The Geological Survey in Scotland*.

National Museum of Wales, Cathays Park, Cardiff CF1 3NP. *Ichthyosaurs: a history of fossil 'sea-dragons'*; *Plants of the Coal Measures swamps*; *'Formed stones', folklore and fossils*, *Trilobites in Wales* and *Fossil plants from Wales*. Most of these are also relevant outside Wales.

Many other excellent geological booklets have been produced by local museums and societies throughout the UK.

Local geology

Each museum should have the following in its library. If there are many geological visitors these publications may be worth selling if they are otherwise unavailable locally.

British Geological Survey (BGS) 1 inch to the mile or 1:50 000 Map Sheets and accompanying Memoirs (published by HMSO) of the area of interest to the museum, in 'Solid' and 'Solid and Drift' versions (that is, with and without superficial deposits such as boulder clay and river gravels). Other Memoirs and Reports, which may not be associated with a particular map, deal with particular aspects of an area such as its water supply or mineral resources. Remember to check for old, out of print editions of maps and memoirs which are often available from dealers such as Stuart Baldwin (see appendix 8).

The local volume in the *British Regional Geology* series published by HMSO for the BGS. (BGS publications and catalogues can be obtained from HMSO or direct from the BGS.)

Any special guides to the area published by the Geologists' Association and by other bodies such as local universities, societies and museums; check with local geologists and the nearest university or polytechnic's geology department, library and bookshop.

Topographic, land use and soil survey maps of the area, available from your local bookshop or Ordnance Survey agent.

Journals

Your museum may have runs of old journals such as those of the Geological Society and Geologists' Association, as well as county and regional societies, and the *Monographs of the Palaeontographical Society*. These are valuable references for local geology and for the identification of specimens. Modern journals tend to be more specialised, with little of the old tradition of general natural history, and the smaller museum will be able to justify the cost of few, if any. Two exceptions are *Geology Today* (section 3.2) and *The Geological Curator* (section 3.1). They are fairly cheap and give a good idea of current affairs in geology as a whole and in museums. If you are interested in site conservation you should get *Earth Science Conservation* published by the NCC.

You should certainly subscribe to local societies or regional journals relevant to your area, such as the *Mercian Geologist* or *Proceedings of the Dorset Natural History and Archaeological Society*.

Appendices

Geological Locality Record Centres

ENGLAND

Avon Bristol Museum
Berkshire Reading Museum
Buckinghamshire County Museum, Aylesbury
Cambridgeshire (Peterborough) Peterborough Museum
Cambridgeshire (South) Cambridge College of Art & Technology
Cheshire Liverpool Museum
Cleveland County Museum, Middlesbrough
Cumbria National Park Centre, Brockhole
Derbyshire Derby Museum
Devon (East) Exeter Museum
Devon (West) Plymouth Museum
Dorset County Museum, Dorchester
Durham Sunderland Museum
Essex Passmore Edwards Museum, London
Gloucestershire Bristol Museum
Gloucestershire (Forest of Dean) Environmental Studies Centre, Micheldean
Hampshire County Museum Service, Winchester
Hertfordshire (North) North Herts Museum Service, Hitchin
Hertfordshire (South) St Albans Museum
Humberside (South) Scunthorpe Museum
Isle of Man Manx Museum, Douglas
Isle of Wight Museum of Isle of Wight Geology, Sandown
Kent (East) Canterbury Museum
Kent (West) Goldsmith's College, London
Lancashire Liverpool Museum
Lancashire County Museum, Preston
Lancashire (Bolton) Bolton Museum
Leicestershire Leicestershire Museums, Leicester
Lincolnshire (North) Scunthorpe Museum
Manchester Manchester Museum
Merseyside Liverpool Museum
Norfolk Castle Museum, Norwich
Northumberland (North) Hancock Museum, Newcastle
Northumberland (South) Sunderland Museum
Nottinghamshire Wollaton Hall, Nottingham
Shropshire County Museum, Ludlow
Somerset Bristol Museum
Staffordshire Stoke-on-Trent Museum
Suffolk Ipswich Museum
Surrey Kingston Polytechnic
Sussex Brighton Museum

Warwickshire Warwickshire Museum
West Midlands (Dudley) Dudley Museum
Wiltshire Bristol Museum
Yorkshire, North Yorkshire Museum, York
Yorkshire, South (Doncaster) Doncaster Museum
Yorkshire, South (Sheffield) Sheffield Museum
Yorkshire, West (Bradford) Cliffe Castle Museum, Keighley
Yorkshire, West (Kirklees) Bagshaw Museum, Batley
Yorkshire, West (Leeds) Leeds Museum

NORTHERN IRELAND Ulster Museum, Belfast

SCOTLAND

Grampian (Banff) Peterhead Museum
Grampian (Buchan) Peterhead Museum
Isle of Skye Field Centre, Broadford, Skye
Strathclyde (Renfrewshire) Paisley Museum
Tayside Dundee Museum
Tayside (Angus) Montrose Museum
Tayside (Perth) Perth Museum

WALES

Clwyd Liverpool Museum

A simple stratigraphic classification

The following gives only an outline of British stratigraphy. For more detail first see the British Museum (Natural History) publications *British Cainozoic Fossils*, *British Mesozoic Fossils* and *British Palaeozoic Fossils*. Specific information on the exact correlation of British rocks can be found in a series of special reports produced by the Geological Society. For information on old names or foreign localities, see the *Lexique Stratigraphique International* (ed D Curry).

In the table below an * denotes that the example given overlaps an epoch boundary, eg the Bracklesham Beds cross the boundary between the Middle and Upper Eocene, but for convenience are put in the former category. The ages given in millions of years are subject to an uncertainty of 10 to 15 million years for divisions older than 160 million years. There is some controversy over whether the Tremadoc Epoch should be included in the Cambrian or Ordovician Eras – it is here placed in the former.

ERA	PERIOD	EPOCH or AGE	Examples of British Strata	Age in millions of years
CAINOZOIC	Quaternary (Ice age)	Holocene	Flandrian (post glacial)	
		Pleistocene Upper	Devensian (last glacial) Ipswichian (interglacial) Wolstonian (glacial)	
		Middle	Hoxnian (interglacial) Anglian (glacial) Cromerian (interglacial)	
		Lower	eg Weybourne Crag eg Chillesford Crag eg Norwich Crag eg Red Crag	
	Tertiary Upper or Neogene	Pliocene	eg Coralline Crag eg St Erth Beds	2
		Miocene		
	Lower or Palaeogene	Oligocene	eg Bovey Tracey Beds eg Hamstead Beds	25
		Eocene Upper	eg Bembridge Beds eg Osborne Beds eg Headon Beds eg Barton & Hengistbury Beds	38
		Middle	eg *Bracklesham Beds eg Bournemouth Beds eg Boscombe Sands	42
		Lower	eg Bagshot Sands eg Claygate Beds eg London Clay eg Blackheath & Oldhaven Beds eg Woolwich & Reading Beds	50
		Palaeocene	eg Thanet Beds	55

MESOZOIC

Period	Series	Stage	Beds
Cretaceous	Upper	Maastrichtian *Senonian	Upper Chalk
		Turonian	Middle Chalk
		Cenomanian	Lower Chalk
	Lower	Albian, Upper / Middle / Lower	Upper Greensand / Gault / Lower Greensand
		Aptian	
		Barremian	eg Wealden & Speeton Clay
		Hauterian	
		Valanginian	
		Berriasian	

98

144

Period	Series	Stage	Beds
Jurassic	Upper	*Portlandian	Purbeck Bed / Portland Beds
		Kimmeridgian	Kimmeridge Clay
		Oxfordian	Corallian & Ampthill Clay
		Callovian	*Oxford Clay & Kellaways
	Middle	Bathonian	Great Oolite & *U. Estuarine
		Bajocian	*Inferior Oolite
		Aalenian	
	Lower	Toarcian	Upper Lias
		Pliensbachian Upper	Middle Lias
		Lower	
		Sinemurian	Lower Lias
		Hettangian	

163

188

213

Period	Series	Stage	Beds
Triassic	Upper	Rhaetian	eg Rhaetic
	Middle		eg Keuper Marl
	Lower		eg *Bunter Sandstone

219

Permian	Zechstein	eg Magnesian Limestone	
	Rotliegendes		286
Carboniferous	Stephanian	Coal Measures	
	Westphalian		
	Namurian	Millstone Grit	
	Visean	Carboniferous Limestone	
	Tournaisian		360
Devonian		Old Red Sandstone	408
Silurian	Pridoli	eg Ludlow Bone bed	
	Ludlow	eg Ludlow shale, Aymestry L'st	
	Wenlock	eg Wenlock limestone	
	Llandovery		438
Ordovician	Ashgill		
	Caradoc		
	Llandeilo		
	Llanvirn		
	Arenig		505
Cambrian	Tremadoc		
Upper	Merioneth		
Middle	St Davids		
Lower	Comley		590

PALAEOZOIC

Precambrian

A simple biological classification for organising fossil collections

Plants
Protozoa (foraminifera etc – uncommon)
Sponges
Archaeocyathids (uncommon)
Stromatoporoids (uncommon)
Cnidarians (corals mainly)
Bryozoa ('moss animals' or polyzoa)
Brachiopods
Molluscs
   Bivalves (=lamellibranchs)
   Gastropods (snails)
   Cephalopods
      Nautiloids
      Goniatites
      Ammonites
      Belemnites
Echinoderms
   Sea Urchins
   Starfish and Brittlestars
   Crinoids (sea lilies)
Arthropods
   Crustacea
   Trilobites
   Insects
Graptolites
Worms and other misc. invertebrates
Vertebrates
   Fish
   Amphibians
   Reptiles
   Birds
   Mammals
Trace fossils (burrows, footprints etc)
Fossils awaiting sorting or indeterminate

Igneous rocks

4.1 Classification of Igneous Rocks

1 Fine grained (crystals not visible to naked eye – lavas)
 1.1 Pyroclastics
 1.2 Obsidian to rhyolite
 1.3 Keratophyre to andesite
 1.4 Basalt
 1.5 Feldspathoid lavas
 1.6 Ultrabasics

2 Coarse grained (crystals visible)
 2.1 Pegmatites and granites
 2.2 Syenites and diorites
 2.3 Gabbro etc
 2.4 Norite etc
 2.5 Ultramafics

3 Igneous structures (xenoliths, contacts, ropey lava etc)

Unsorted or unnamed rocks can be easily allocated to 1 or 2.

4.2 Lexicon of Igneous Rocks

adamellite	2.1	biotitite	2.5	diorite	2.2
aegerinite	2.5	blue ground	2.5	ditroite	2.2
agglomerate	1.1	bojite	2.3	dolerite	2.3
allivalite	2.3	borolanite	2.2	dungannonite	2.2
alnoite	2.3	bostonite	2.2	dunite	2.5
analcite basanite	1.5	breccia, volcanic	1.1	elvan	2.1
analcite syenite	2.2	bronzitite	2.5	enderbite	2.1
andesinite	2.2	camptonite	2.3	essexite	2.3
andesite	1.3	cancrinite syenite	2.2	eucrite	2.3
ankaramite	1.4	carbonatite	1.5	fayalite pitchstone	1.2
anorthosite	2.5	charnockite	2.1	felsite	2.1
aplite	2.1	chibinite	2.2	fenite	1.5
appinite	2.2	chromitite	2.5	ferguiste	2.2
ash	1.1	clinopyroxenite	2.3	ferrogabbro	2.3
augitite	2.5	corsite	2.3	foyaite	2.2
autobreccia	1.1	corundum syenite	2.2	gabbro	2.3
banakite	1.4	cossyrite	2.2	glenmuirite	2.3
banatite	2.2	crinanite	2.3	glimmerite	2.5
basalt	1.4	crystal tuff	1.1	granite	2.1
basanite	1.4	dacite	1.2	granodiorite	2.1
basanitoid	1.5	diabase	2.3	granophyre	2.1
biotite pyroxenite	2.5	diallagite	2.5	greisen	2.1

grorudite	2.1	melmafite	1.5	pulaskite	2.2
harzburgite	2.5	melteigite	2.2	pyroxenite	2.5
hauynophyre	1.5	micaite	2.5	quartz porphyry	2.1
hawaiite	1.3	microadamellite	2.1	rhomb porphyry	2.2
hornblendite	2.5	microdiorite	2.2	rhyodacite	1.2
hypersthenite	2.5	micro *see under*		rhyolite	1.2
ignimbrite	1.1	*second part of name*		scyelite	2.5
ijolite	2.4	minette	2.3	serpentinite	2.5
italite	1.5	missourite	2.2	shonkinite	2.2
kalmafite	1.5	monchiquite	2.3	sodalite syenite	2.4
katungite	1.5	monmouthite	2.2	spessartite	2.3
kentallenite	2.3	monzonite	2.2	spilite	1.3
keratophyre	2.2	mugearite	1.3	syenite	2.2
kenyte	2.2	napoleonite	2.3	syenite aplite	2.1
kersantite	2.3	nemafite	1.5	syenite pegmatite	2.1
kimberlite	2.5	nepheline syenite	2.2	syenodiorite	2.2
kylite	2.4	nevadite	1.2	syenogabbro	2.3
lamprophyre	2.3	nordmarkite	2.2	tachylyte	1.4
larvikite	2.2	norite	2.4	tephrite	1.5
latite	2.2	obsidian	1.2	teschenite	2.3
laurvigite	2.2	okaite	2.3	teschenite basalt	2.3
ledmorite	2.2	oligoclasite	2.2	theralite	2.4
leucitite	1.5	olivinite	2.5	tholeiite	1.4
leucitophyre	1.5	orthogabbro	2.3	tinguaite	2.2
leucodiorite	2.2	orthophyre	2.2	tonalite	2.2
leumafite	1.5	orthopyroxenite	2.4	tosconite	1.2
litchfieldite	2.2	orthotrachyte	1.3	trachyandesite	1.3
lugarite	2.3	pantellerite	1.2	trachybasalt	1.4
luxullianite	2.1	pegmatite	2.1	trachyte	1.3
madupite	1.5	peridotite	2.5	troctolite	2.3
mafurite	1.5	perthosite	2.2	tuff	1.1
malignite	2.2	phonolite	1.3	turjaite	2.3
mariupolite	2.2	picrite	2.5	tuvinite	1.5
markfieldite	2.2	pitchstone	1.2	ugandite	1.5
marscoite	2.2	plumasite	2.2	urtite	2.4
melanite	2.2	porphyrite	2.2	vogesite	2.3
melilitite	1.5	porphyry	2.2	websterite	2.5

Classification of metamorphic rocks

1 Slates
2 Schists, phyllites
3 Gneisses, migmatites
4 Hornfels
5 Marble
6 Quartzite, halleflinta
7 Misc. other metamorphic rocks
8 Metamorphic structures
9 Unsorted metamorphics

APPENDIX 6
Sedimentary rocks

6.1 Classification of sedimentary rocks

1 Rudaceous (pebbly) = conglomerates, breccias, pebbles.
2 Arenaceous (sandy) = sandstones, sand, greywackes.
3 Argillaceous (clayey) = shales, clays, muds, mudstone, marls.
4 Carbonates (lime rich) = limestones, oolites, chalk, stalactites, dolomites.
5 Ferruginous (iron rich) = ironstones.
6 Carbonaceous (plant rich) = coal, peat, oil shale.
7 Phosphatic (phosphate rich) = bone beds, guano, coprolite.
8 Evaporites – rock salt, gypsum (= minerals also).
9 Misc. others – soils, laterite, residual deposits.
10 Sedimentary structures = ripple marks, desiccation cracks, nodules etc (trace fossils see biological classification).
11 Sedimentary rocks awaiting sorting.

6.2 Lexicon of sedimentary rocks

anhydrite rock	8	diatomite	9	nodule	10
anthracite	6	dolomite	4	oil shale	6
arenite	2	durain	6	oolite	4
argillite	3	evaporite	8	oolitic ironstone	5
arkose	2	fanglomerate	1	oolitic limestone	4
bauxite	9	flagstone	10	ooze	9
bedding plane	10	flysch	2	orthoquartzite	2
biopelite	3	flint	9	peat	6
black shale	3	fusain	6	pelite	3
boghead coal	6	ganister	2	pisolite	4
bog iron	5	graded bedding	10	porcellanite	4
bone bed	7	gravel	1	psammite	2
breccia	1	greywacke	2	rain print	10
calcarenite	4	greensand	2	ripple marks	10
calcilutite	4	grit	2	rudite	1
calcirudite	4	humus	6	sandstone	2
caliche	4	ironstone	5	septarian	10
chalk	4	klintite	4	shale	3
chamosite oolite	5	laterite	9	siltstone	3
chert	9	lignite	6	stylolite	10
clay	3	limestone	4	subgreywacke	3
clay ironstone	5	marl	3	till	1
claystone	3	molasse	2	tillite	1
coal	6	mud	3	tracks see fossils	
concretion	10	mud ball	10	travertine	4
conglomerate	1	mud cracks	10	tufa	4
cross bedding	10	mudstone	3	vitrain	6

124

Minerals

7.1 Classification of minerals

Minerals are classified according to their chemistry and crystal structure. The system used here has been devised specifically to meet the needs of this book. In this classification the non-silicates are based on J F Ferraiolo, 'A systematic classification of non-silicate minerals', *Bulletin of the American Museum of Natural History 172*, 1982. The silicates are based on H Strunz, *Mineralogische Tabellen*, 1970. M Fleischer, *Glossary of Mineral Species*, 1987, has been used to check the compositions of mineral groups and the spelling of valid species names. This classification has been adapted to comply with the recommendations of the IMA Commission on New Minerals and Mineral Names.

The numbers allocated to each mineral are for cross-referencing purposes only. Those given to the non-silicates are from Ferraiolo. The other groups have been allocated numbers in multiples of 10. The system is organised as follows:

Non-silicates	elements & alloys	01
	sulphides & sulphosalts	02 & 03
	oxides & hydroxides	04–08
	halides	09–12
	carbonates	13–17
	nitrates	18–20
	borates	24–27
	sulphates	28–32
	selenates, tellurates etc	33–34
	chromates	35–36
	phosphates, arsenates & vanadates	37–43
	antimonates	44
	antimonites	45–46
	vanadium oxysalts	47
	molybdates & tungstates	48–49
	oxylates, melilates etc	50
Silica		60
Silicates		70–120
Organic substances		130
Unidentified specimens		140

Names printed in bold are valid species names; names printed in capitals are group names; names printed in italics are acceptable varieties; names not printed as above are organic substances, mixtures, rocks, and general or discredited names.

When referring to varieties they should be written after the species to which they belong, eg quartz var. amethyst. Only the commoner names are included in the following tables. If your collection is labelled with chemical names (eg red chromate of lead) then you will need expert help. Details of old names etc found on labels should at least be recorded in history files.

The following table gives the classification in detail. Appendix 7.2 gives an index to this table as well as listing mineral synonyms, special environmental needs and any associated hazards.

ELEMENTS & ALLOYS

gold	1
silver	1
copper	1
mercury	1
moschellandsbergite	1
iron	1
awaruite	1
lead	1
platinum	1
arsenic	1
stibarsen	1
antimony	1
bismuth	1
sulphur	1
diamond	1
graphite	1

SULPHIDES & SULPHOSALTS

argentite	2
acanthite	2
chalcocite	2
djurleite	2
bornite	2
joseite	2
pentlandite	2
galena	2
clausthalite	2
zorgite	2
alabandite	2
sphalerite	2
wurtzite	2
greenockite	2
pyrrhotite	2
nickeline	2
covellite	2

cinnabar	2
millerite	2
realgar	2
chalcopyrite	2
stannite	2
orpiment	2
stibnite	2
bismuthinite	2
tellurobismuthite	2
tetradymite	2
nagyagite	2
pyrite	2
marcasite	2
cobaltite	2
gersdorffite	2
arsenopyrite	2
löllingite	2
glaucodot	2
molybdenite	2
sylvanite	2
skutterudite	2
nickel-skutterudite	2
kermesite	2
kesterite	2
polybasite	3
enargite	3
stephanite	3
tennantite	3
tetrahedrite	3
proustite	3
pyrargyrite	3
bournonite	3
aikinite	3
jamesonite	3
zinkenite	3

OXIDES & HYDROXIDES

cuprite	4
zincite	4
tenorite	4
corundum	4
emery	4
hematite	4
perovskite	4
ilmenite	4
senarmontite	4
valentinite	4
rutile	4
pyrolusite	4
psilomelane	4
wad	4
cassiterite	4
anatase	4
brookite	4
gummite	5
uraninite	5
diaspore	6
goethite	6
limonite	6
lepidocrocite	6
manganite	6
bauxite	6
brucite	6
gibbsite	6
spinel	7
gahnite	7
magnetite	7
franklinite	7
chromite	7
hausmannite	7
minium	7
chrysoberyl	7
braunite	7

MOLYBDATES & TUNGSTATES	
wolframite	48
scheelite	48
wulfenite	48

SILICA

tridymite	60
quartz	60
chalcedony	60
opal	60

SILICATES

phenacite	70
willemite	70
OLIVINE GROUP	
forsterite	70
olivine	70
GARNET GROUP	
garnet	70
pyrope	70
almandine	70
spessartine	70
grossular	70
andradite	70
uvarovite	70
zircon	70
thorite	70
euclase	70
sillimanite	70
andalusite	70
kyanite	70
topaz	70
staurolite	70
chondrodite	70
humite	70
clinohumite	70
titanite	70
cerite	70
chloritoid	70
ottrelite	70
datolite	70
gadolinite	70
gehlenite	80
melilite	80
ilvaite	80
bertrandite	80
hemimorphite	80

wöhlerite	80
clinozoisite	80
epidote	80
piemontite	80
allanite	80
zoisite	80
vesuvianite	80
eudialite	90
AXINITE	90
beryl	90
cordierite	90
TOURMALINE	90
dioptase	90
PYROXENE GROUP	
pyroxene	100
diopside	100
hedenbergite	100
aegirine	100
augite	100
omphacite	100
jadeite	100
spodumene	100
enstatite	100
diallage	100
AMPHIBOLE GROUP	
amphibole	100
cummingtonite	100
grunerite	100
amosite	100
tremolite	100
actinolite	100
hornblende	100
pargasite	100
glaucophane	100
riebeckite	100
richterite	100
anthophyllite	100
wollastonite	100
bustamite	100
pectolite	100
okenite	100
rhodonite	100
babingtonite	100
meliphanite	110
prehnite	110
astrophyllite	110
APOPHYLLITE	110
pyrophyllite	110
talc	110

MICA GROUP	
mica	110
paragonite	110
muscovite	110
glauconite	110
celadonite	110
phlogopite	110
biotite	110
lepidolite	110
zinnwaldite	110
margarite	110
clintonite	110
clay	110
illite	110
montmorillonite	110
vermiculite	110
CHLORITE GROUP	
chlorite	110
cookeite	110
clinochlore	110
chamosite	110
pennantite	110
kaolinite	110
SERPENTINE GROUP	
serpentine	110
antigorite	110
lizardite	110
chrysotile	110
garnierite	110
cronstedtite	110
chrysocolla	110
allophane	110
PYROSMALITE	110
palygorskite	110
sepiolite	110
gyrolite	110
nepheline	120
petalite	120
analcime	120
leucite	120
pollucite	120
FELDSPAR GROUP	
feldspar	120
sanidine	120
orthoclase	120
microcline	120
hyalophane	120
celsian	120
anorthoclase	120

plagioclase	120	meionite	120	chabazite	120
albite	120	sarcolite	120		
oligoclase	120	ZEOLITE GROUP		**ORGANICS**	
andesine	120	zeolite	120		
labradorite	120	mesotype	120	amber	130
bytownite	120	natrolite	120	copal	130
anorthite	120	scolecite	120	elaterite	130
cancrinite	120	mesolite	120	bitumen	130
davyne	120	thomsonite	120	asphalt	130
sodalite	120	laumontite	120	lignite	130
nosean	120	heulandite	120	jet	130
hauyne	120	stilbite	120	anthracite	130
lazurite	120	epistilbite	120	coal	130
lapis lazuli	120	brewsterite	120		
SCAPOLITE		gismondine	120	**SPECIMENS**	
GROUP		phillipsite	120	**AWAITING**	
scapolite	120	harmotome	120	**IDENTI-**	
marialite	120	gmelinite	120	**FICATION**	140

7.2 Lexicon of minerals including their environmental requirements and associated health hazards

acanthite 05 (sulphides). Keep in dark.

achroite colourless variety of TOURMALINE

acmite synonym of **aegirine**

actinolite 100 (silicates – AMPHIBOLE group) asbestos: avoid inhalation, keep in sealed container.

adamite 41 (phosphates, arsenates & vanadates)

adularia variety of **orthoclase**

aegirine 100 (silicates – PYROXENE group)

agate banded variety of **quartz** var. *chalcedony*

aikinite 03 (sulphosalts)

alabandite 02 (sulphides). Control humidity. Keep in dark.

alabaster massive, fine-grained variety of **gypsum**. Very soft, handle with care.

albite 120 (silicates – FELDSPAR group)

alexandrite variety of **chrysoberyl** (appears red under tungsten lighting, green under fluorescent lighting or in daylight).

allanite 80 (silicates)

allemontite synonym of **stibarsen**

allophane 110 (silicates)

almandine 70 (silicates – GARNET group)

alstonite 14 (carbonates)

alum 29 (sulphates) Water-soluble, toxic; occurs naturally but commonly manufactured to fake 'fluorite'.

aluminite 31 (sulphates)

alumstone synonym of **alunite**

alunite 30 (sulphates). Control humidity to prevent dehydration and cracking.

129

amalgam	synonym of **moschellandsbergite** OR a mercury-rich variety of **silver**
amazonite or *amazonstone*	green variety of **microcline**
amber	130 (organics)
amethyst	purple variety of **quartz**. May fade in strong light.
amosite	100 (silicates – AMPHIBOLE group) asbestiform variety of **grunerite** or **anthophyllite**. Avoid inhalation, keep in sealed container.
AMPHIBOLE	100 (silicates) group name
analcime	120 (silicates)
analcite	synonym of **analcime**
anatase	04 (oxides & hydroxides)
andalusite	70 (silicates)
andesine	120 (silicates – FELDSPAR group)
andradite	70 (silicates – GARNET group)
anglesite	28 (sulphates). Toxic. Some localities change colour on exposure to light.
anhydrite	28 (sulphates). Control humidity to prevent hydration. Some localities change colour on exposure to light.
ankerite	14 (carbonates)
annabergite	40 (phosphates, arsenates & vanadates)
anorthite	120 (silicates – FELDSPAR group)
anorthoclase	120 (silicates – FELDSPAR group)
anthophyllite	100 (silicates – AMPHIBOLE group) asbestos: avoid inhalation, keep in sealed container.
anthracite	130 (organics)
antigorite	110 (silicates – SERPENTINE group)
antimonite	synonym of **stibnite**
antimony	01 (elements & alloys). Toxic.
APATITE	41 (phosphates, arsenates & vanadates). Group name, includes **fluorapatite, chlorapatite, hydroxylapatite** and **carbonate-fluorapatite**, but has been widely used as a synonym of **fluorapatite**, the most common of the APATITE species.
APOPHYLLITE	110 (silicates). Group name, includes **fluorapophyllite, hydroxyapophyllite** and **natroapophyllite**.
aquamarine	blue or bluish-green variety of **beryl**
aragonite	14 (carbonates)
argentite	02 (sulphides). Specimens labelled **argentite** are **acanthite**; **argentite** is only stable at temperatures above 177°C. Keep in dark.
arsenic	01 (elements & alloys). Control humidity. Toxic.
arsenopyrite	02 (sulphides). Control humidity.
artinite	16 (carbonates) fibrous crystals, handle with care.
asbestos	variety of **chrysotile** OR **tremolite** OR **actinolite** OR amosite OR **riebeckite** (var. *crocidolite*) OR **anthophyllite** OR **grunerite** OR **cummingtonite**. Avoid inhalation, keep in sealed container.
asphalt	130 (organics)
astrophyllite	110 (silicates)

atacamite	10 (halides)
augite	100 (silicates – PYROXENE group)
aurichalcite	16 (carbonates) fibrous crystals, handle with care.
automolite	synonym of **gahnite**
autunite	40 (phosphates, arsenates & vanadates). May be radioactive. Control humidity to prevent dehydration and disintegration.
avanturine	mis-spelling of *aventurine*
aventurine	variety of **quartz** or **oligoclase** (**oligoclase** var. *sunstone* = aventurine FELDSPAR)
awaruite	01 (elements & alloys)
AXINITE	90 (silicates). Group name, includes **ferro-axinite**, **magnesio-axinite**, and **manganaxinite**.
azurite	16 (carbonates). May darken on exposure to light.
babingtonite	100 (silicates)
balas ruby	gem name for red **spinel**
barite	28 (sulphates). Some localities change colour on exposure to light.
baryte	synonym of **barite** (both names acceptable)
barytes	synonym of **barite**
barytocalcite	14 (carbonates)
basaluminite	31 (sulphates)
bastite	variety of **enstatite** (altered **enstatite**)
bauxite	06 (oxides & hydroxides). A rock containing mixed oxides and hydroxides of aluminium.
bayldonite	41 (phosphates, arsenates & vanadates)
beekite	variety of **quartz**
bentonite	a rock composed mainly of **montmorillonite**
bertrandite	80 (silicates)
beryl	90 (silicates)
bindheimite	44 (antimonates)
biotite	110 (silicates – MICA group)
bismuth	01 (elements & alloys). Readily tarnishes.
bismuthinite	02 (sulphides). Readily tarnishes.
bitumen	130 (organics)
black jack	synonym of **sphalerite**
black lead	synonym of **graphite**
blende	synonym of **sphalerite**
blistered copper	botryoidal variety of **chalcopyrite**
blomstrandine	synonym of **uranpyrochlore**
bloodstone (= *heliotrope*)	variety of **quartz** var. *chalcedony*
blue asbestos	synonym of **riebeckite** var. *crocidolite*
blue john	variety of **fluorite**
blue vitriol	synonym of **chalcanthite**
boracite	25 (borates). Control humidity to prevent efflorescence.
borax	26 (borates). Toxic. Control humidity to prevent efflorescence.
bornite	02 (sulphides). Readily tarnishes.
bournonite	03 (sulphosalts)
brandisite	synonym of **clintonite**

braunite	07 (oxides & hydroxides)
breunnerite	variety of **magnesite**
brewsterite	120 (silicates – ZEOLITE group)
brochantite	30 (sulphates)
bromargyrite	09 (halides). Keep in dark.
bromyrite	synonym of **bromargyrite**
brookite	04 (oxides & hydroxides)
bronzite	synonym of **enstatite**
brown haematite	synonym of limonite
brucite	06 (oxides & hydroxides)
burnt amethyst	**quartz** var. *amethyst*, heat-treated to induce a yellow colouring, sometimes sold as 'citrine'.
bustamite	100 (silicates)
bytownite	120 (silicates – FELDSPAR group)
cacholong	variety of **opal**
cacoxenite	42 (phosphates, arsenates & vanadates)
cairngorm	reddish-brown variety of **quartz**
calamine	synonym of **smithsonite** OR **hemimorphite**
calcedony	synonym of *chalcedony*, a variety of **quartz**
calcite	14 (carbonates)
caledonite	32 (sulphates)
calomel	09 (halides)
campylite	variety of **mimetite**
cancrinite	120 (silicates)
carbonado	black variety of **diamond**
carbonate of barytes	synonym of **witherite**
carinthine	variety of hornblende
carnallite	11 (halides). Control humidity to prevent deliquescence.
carnelian	variety of **quartz** var. *chalcedony*
cassiterite	04 (oxides & hydroxides)
cats-eye	usually a variety of **quartz** OR **chrysoberyl**, but other species may rarely show 'chatoyancy', a single linear play of light due to reflections from microscopic parallel inclusions or a fibrous structure.
celadonite	110 (silicates – MICA group)
celestine	28 (sulphates). Some localities change colour on exposure to light (usually reversible).
celestite	synonym of **celestine**
celsian	120 (silicates – FELDSPAR group)
cerargyrite	synonym of **chlorargyrite**, but has been used as a group name for the silver halides. Keep in dark.
cerite	70 (silicates)
ceruleite	42 (phosphates, arsenates & vanadates)
cerussite	14 (carbonates)
ceylonite	variety of **spinel**
chabazite	120 (silicates – ZEOLITE group)
chalcanthite	29 (sulphates). Toxic. Control humidity to prevent efflorescence.
chalcedony	60 (silica) variety of **quartz**
chalcocite	02 (sulphides). Keep fresh, untarnished material in dark.

chalcolite	synonym of **torbernite**
chalcophyllite	43 (phosphates, arsenates & vanadates)
chalcopyrite	02 (sulphides). Readily tarnishes.
chalcosiderite	42 (phosphates, arsenates & vanadates)
chalcosine	synonym of **chalcocite** (both names acceptable)
chalcotrichite	fibrous variety of **cuprite**. Delicate, handle with care.
chalybite	synonym of **siderite**
chamosite	110 (silicates – CHLORITE group)
chert	variety of **quartz** var. *chalcedony*
chessylite	synonym of **azurite**
chiastolite	variety of **andalusite**
childrenite	42 (phosphates, arsenates & vanadates)
chile saltpetre	synonym of **nitratine**
china clay	synonym of **kaolinite**
chloanthite	variety of **nickel-skutterudite**
chlorargyrite	09 (halides). Keep in dark.
CHLORITE	110 (silicates) group name
chloritoid	70 (silicates)
chondrodite	70 (silicates)
chromite	07 (oxides & hydroxides)
chrysoberyl	07 (oxides & hydroxides)
chrysocolla	110 (silicates). Control humidity to prevent dehydration and shrinkage.
chrysolite	synonym of OLIVINE
chrysoprase	variety of **quartz** var. *chalcedony*. Fades in strong light.
chrysotile	110 (silicates – SERPENTINE group) includes **clinochrysotile**, **orthochrysotile**, and **parachrysotile**. Asbestos: avoid inhalation, keep in sealed container.
cinnabar	02 (sulphides). Toxic. Keep in dark.
cinnamon-stone	synonym of *hessonite*, a var, of **grossular**
citrine	yellow variety of **quartz**
clausthalite	02 (sulphides)
clay	110 (silicates) general name
cleavelandite	lamellar variety of **albite**
clinochlore	110 (silicates – CHLORITE group)
clinoclase	41 (phosphates, arsenates & vanadates)
clinoclasite	synonym of **clinoclase**
clinohumite	70 (silicates)
clinozoisite	80 (silicates)
clintonite	110 (silicates – MICA group)
coal	130 (organics)
cobalt bloom	synonym of **erythrite**
cobalt glance	synonym of **cobaltite**
cobaltite	02 (sulphides). Readily tarnishes.
cobaltocalcite	synonym of **spherocobaltite**
coccolite	iron-rich variety of **augite**
colemanite	26 (borates). Toxic.
collophane	massive fine-grained variety of APATITE
columbite	08 (oxides & hydroxides)
conichalcite	41 (phosphates, arsenates & vanadates)

cookeite	110 (silicates – CHLORITE group)
copal	130 (organics)
copper	01 (elements & alloys). Readily tarnishes.
copper glance	synonym of **chalcocite**
copper pyrites	synonym of **chalcopyrite**
copper-nickel	synonym of **nickeline**
cordierite	90 (silicates)
corundum	04 (oxides & hydroxides)
cotterite	variety of **quartz**
covelline	synonym of **covellite** (both names acceptable)
covellite	02 (sulphides)
crocidolite	asbestiform variety of **riebeckite**. Avoid inhalation, keep in sealed container.
crocoite	35 (chromates). Keep in dark.
cronstedtite	110 (silicates)
cryolite	11 (halides)
cummingtonite	100 (silicates – AMPHIBOLE group) asbestos: avoid inhalation, keep in sealed container.
cuprite	04 (oxides & hydroxides). Keep in dark.
cuprouranite	synonym of **torbernite**
cyanite	synonym of **kyanite**
cymophane (= *cats-eye*)	variety of **chrysoberyl**
cyprine	variety of **idocrase**
daphnite	variety of **chamosite**
datolite	70 (silicates)
davyne	120 (silicates)
delessite	variety of **clinochlore**
demantoid	verdant green variety of **andradite**
descloizite	41 (phosphates, arsenates & vanadates)
desert rose	usually a variety of **gypsum** OR **barite**. **Gypsum:** very soft, handle with care.
desmine	synonym of **stilbite**
devilline	31 (sulphates)
diallage	100 (silicates), general term for AMPHIBOLES or PYROXENES OR for altered PYROXENES.
diamond	01 (elements & alloys)
diaspore	06 (oxides & hydroxides)
dichroite	synonym of **cordierite**
diopside	100 (silicates – PYROXENE group)
dioptase	90 (silicates)
dipyre	variety of SCAPOLITE
disthene	synonym of **kyanite**
djurleite	02 (sulphides)
dogtooth spar	variety of **calcite**
dolomite	14 (carbonates)
dravite	90 (silicates – TOURMALINE group) see TOURMALINE
dysanalyte	variety of **perovskite**
egyptian jasper	variety of **quartz** var. *chalcedony*
eisenkiesel	variety of **quartz**

134

elaterite	130 (organics)
elbaite	90 (silicates – TOURMALINE group) see TOUR-MALINE
embolite	bromian variety of **chlorargyrite**. Keep in dark.
emerald	verdant green (chrome-bearing) variety of **beryl**
emery	04 (oxides & hydroxides) mixture of **corundum** and **magnetite**
enargite	03 (sulphosalts). Readily tarnishes.
endlichite	variety of **vanadinite**
enstatite	100 (silicates – PYROXENE group)
epidote	80 (silicates)
epistilbite	120 (silicates – ZEOLITE group)
epsomite	29 (sulphates). Control humidity to prevent efflorescence.
erubescite	synonym of **bornite**
erythrite	40 (phosphates, arsenates & vanadates). Keep in dark.
essonite	synonym of *hessonite*, a variety of **grossular**
euclase	70 (silicates)
eudialite	90 (silicates)
euxenite	08 (oxides & hydroxides). May be radioactive. Control humidity to prevent hydration.
faroelite (= *mesole*)	variety of **thomsonite**
fassaite	variety of **diopside** OR **augite**
FELDSPAR	120 (silicates) group name
felspar	synonym of FELDSPAR
fergusonite	08 (oxides & hydroxides). Control humidity to prevent hydration.
fibroferrite	31 (sulphates)
fibrolite	synonym of **sillimanite**
flint	variety of **quartz** var. *chalcedony*
flos ferri	variety of **aragonite**
fluor	synonym of **fluorite**
fluorapatite	41 (phosphates, arsenates & vanadates – APATITE group). Some localities change colour on exposure to light.
fluorite	09 (halides). Some localities change colour on exposure to light.
fluorspar	synonym of **fluorite**
forsterite	70 (silicates – OLIVINE group)
francolite	synonym of **carbonate-fluorapatite**, see APATITE.
franklinite	07 (oxides & hydroxides)
fuchsite	verdant green (chrome-bearing) variety of **muscovite**
fullers earth	synonym of **montmorillonite**, and sometimes of other clay minerals
gadolinite	70 (silicates)
gahnite	07 (oxides & hydroxides)
galena	02 (sulphides). Readily tarnishes.
GARNET	70 (silicates) group name
garnierite	110 (silicates – SERPENTINE group)
gearksutite	11 (halides)

gehlenite	80 (silicates)
genthite	synonym of **garnierite**
gersdorffite	02 (sulphides). Control humidity.
gibbsite	06 (oxides & hydroxides)
gilbertite	variety of **muscovite**
gismondine	120 (silicates – ZEOLITE group)
glauber's salt	synonym of **mirabilite**
glaucodot	02 (sulphides)
glauconite	110 (silicates – MICA group)
glaucophane	100 (silicates – AMPHIBOLE group)
gmelinite	120 (silicates – ZEOLITE group)
goethite	06 (oxides & hydroxides)
gold	01 (elements & alloys)
goshenite	colourless variety of **beryl**
graphic tellurium	synonym of **sylvanite**
graphite	01 (elements & alloys). Very soft, handle with care.
green earth	synonym of **glauconite** OR **celadonite**
greenockite	02 (sulphides)
grey copper	synonym of **tetrahedrite**, but also seems to have been used for other copper sulphides, especially **chalcocite**.
grossular	70 (silicates – GARNET group)
grunerite	100 (silicates – AMPHIBOLE group) asbestos: avoid inhalation, keep in sealed container.
grünlingite	mixture of **joseite** and **bismuthinite**
gummite	05 (oxides & hydroxides) general term for secondary uranium oxides, often mixtures. Radioactive.
gypsum	29 (sulphates). Very soft, handle with care.
gyrolite	110 (silicates)
hackmanite	variety of **sodalite**. Colour changes on exposure to light (reversible). Keep in dark.
haematite	synonym of **hematite**
halite	09 (halides). Control humidity to prevent deliquescence.
halleflinta	variety of **quartz** var. *chalcedony*
harmotome	120 (silicates – ZEOLITE group)
hausmannite	07 (oxides & hydroxides)
hauyne	120 (silicates)
hawks-eye	variety of **quartz**
hedenbergite	100 (silicates – PYROXENE group)
hedyphane	41 (phosphates, arsenates & vanadates)
heliodor	yellow variety of **beryl**
heliotrope (= *bloodstone*)	variety of **quartz** var. *chalcedony*
hematite	04 (oxides & hydroxides)
hemimorphite	80 (silicates)
henwoodite	synonym of **turquoise**
herrengrundite	synonym of **develline**
hessonite	variety of **grossular**
heulandite	120 (silicates – ZEOLITE group)
hiddenite	green, chrome-bearing variety of **spodumene**
hitchcockite	synonym of **plumbogummite**
hornblende	100 (silicates – AMPHIBOLE group) general name for

136

	calcic AMPHIBOLES, includes **ferrohornblende** and **magnesiohornblende.**
hornstone	variety of **quartz** var. *chalcedony*
humite	70 (silicates)
hyacinth (= jacinth)	orange, red or brownish gem variety of **zircon**
hyalite	variety of **opal**
hyalophane	120 (silicates – FELDSPAR group)
hydrocerussite	16 (carbonates)
hydromagnesite	16 (carbonates). Control humidity to prevent efflorescence.
hydrozincite	16 (carbonates)
hypersthene	synonym of **enstatite** OR **ferrosilite**
iceland spar	variety of **calcite**
idocrase	synonym of **vesuvianite**
illite	110 (silicates) general name.
ilmenite	04 (oxides & hydroxides)
ilvaite	80 (silicates)
indicolite	blue variety of TOURMALINE
iodargyrite	09 (halides). Keep in dark.
iodyrite	synonym of **iodargyrite**
iolite	gem variety of **cordierite**, but has also been widely used as a synonym of **cordierite.**
iron	01 (elements & alloys). Control humidity.
iron glance	specular variety of **hematite**
iron pyrites	synonym of **pyrite**
iserine	variety of **ilmenite**
isostannite	synonym of **kesterite**
jacynth (= *hyacinth*)	orange, red or brownish gem variety of **zircon**
jade	EITHER massive variety of **jadeite** OR **actinolite** var. *nephrite* OR **tremolite** var. *nephrite*
jadeite	100 (silicates – PYROXENE group)
jamesonite	03 (sulphosalts)
jargon or *jargoon*	colourless, yellow or smoky gem variety of **zircon**
jarosite	30 (sulphates)
jasper	variety of **quartz** var. *chalcedony*
jeffersonite	variety of **diopside** OR **augite**
jet	130 (organics)
joseite	02 (sulphides)
kämmererite	variety of **clinochlore**
kaolinite	110 (silicates)
kermesite	02 (sulphides). Red fibrous crystals, handle with care.
kesterite	02 (sulphides)
kidney ore	botryoidal variety of **hematite**
kotchubeite	variety of **clinochlore**
kunzite	lilac-pink gem variety of **spodumene**
kyanite	70 (silicates)
labradorite	120 (silicates – FELDSPAR group)
lanarkite	30 (sulphates)
langite	31 (sulphates)

lapis lazuli	120 (silicates) rock composed of **lazurite, calcite, pyrite** etc.
laumontite	120 (silicates – ZEOLITE group) Control humidity to prevent dehydration and disintegration.
lazulite	41 (phosphates, arsenates & vanadates)
lazurite	120 (silicates)
lead	01 (elements & alloys). Toxic. Control humidity.
lead glance	synonym of **galena**
leadhillite	17 (carbonates)
leonhardite	partially dehydrated variety of **laumontite**
lepidocrocite	06 (oxides & hydroxides)
lepidolite	110 (silicates – MICA group)
lettsomite	synonym of **cyanotrichite**
leucite	120 (silicates)
libethenite	41 (phosphates, arsenates & vanadates)
lignite	130 (organics)
limonite	06 (oxides & hydroxides) general term for hydrous iron oxides, mainly **goethite**
linarite	30 (sulphates)
liroconite	42 (phosphates, arsenates & vanadates)
lithian mica	synonym of **lepidolite**; but not to be confused with lithian **biotite**
lithomarge	massive compact variety of **kaolinite**
lizardite	110 (silicates – SERPENTINE group)
loellingite	synonym of **löllingite**
löllingite	02 (sulphides)
ludlamite	40 (phosphates, arsenates & vanadates)
magnesite	14 (carbonates)
magnetic iron ore	synonym of **magnetite**
magnetic pyrites	synonym of **pyrrhotite**
magnetite	07 (oxides & hydroxides)
malachite	16 (carbonates)
malacon	variety of **zircon** (altered **zircon**)
marmatite	variety of **sphalerite**
manganite	06 (oxides & hydroxides)
marcasite	02 (sulphides). Control humidity.
margarite	110 (silicates – MICA group)
marialite	120 (silicates – SCAPOLITE group)
martite	variety of **hematite** (**hematite** pseudomorphous after **magnetite**)
matlockite	10 (halides)
meerschaum	synonym of **sepiolite**
meionite	120 (silicates – SCAPOLITE group)
melaconite	synonym of **tenorite**
melanterite	29 (sulphates). Control humidity to prevent efflorescence or deliquescence.
melilite	80 (silicates)
meliphanite	110 (silicates)
mendipite	10 (halides)
mercury	01 (elements & alloys). Volatile liquid – if still present,

	toxic.
mesole	synonym of **thomsonite** var. *faroelite*
mesolite	120 (silicates – ZEOLITE group). Fibrous crystals, handle with care.
mesotype	120 (silicates – ZEOLITE group) general name for **natrolite/mesolite/scolecite**, but sometimes (especially in France) used strictly for **natrolite**. Fibrous crystals, handle with care.
metastrengite	synonym of **phosphosiderite**
metatorbernite	40 (phosphates, arsenates & vanadates). May be radioactive.
MICA	110 (silicates) group name
micaceous iron ore	variety of **hematite**
microcline	120 (silicates – FELDSPAR group)
milky quartz	white variety of **quartz**
millerite	02 (sulphides). Golden acicular crystals; handle with care.
mimetite	41 (phosphates, arsenates & vanadates)
minium	07 (oxides & hydroxides). Toxic.
mirabilite	29 (sulphates). Control humidity to prevent efflorescence.
mispickel	synonym of **arsenopyrite**
mizzonite	Variety of SCAPOLITE.
molybdenite	02 (sulphides). Soft, handle with care.
monazite	38 (phosphates, arsenates & vanadates)
montmorillonite	110 (silicates)
moonstone	variety of FELDSPAR, usually **orthoclase** var. *adularia*
morganite	pink variety of **beryl**
morion	black variety of **quartz**
moschellandsbergite	01 (elements & alloys)
moss-agate	variety of **quartz** var. *chalcedony*
mottramite	41 (phosphates, arsenates & vanadates)
mountain leather or mountain cork	variety of **palygorskite** OR asbestos OR pilolite. Asbestos; avoid inhalation, keep in sealed container.
muscovite	110 (silicates – MICA group)
nagyagite	02 (sulphides)
nailhead spar	variety of **calcite**
natrojarosite	30 (sulphates)
natrolite	120 (silicates – ZEOLITE group). Fibrous crystals, handle with care.
natron	15 (carbonates). Toxic. Control humidity to prevent efflorescence.
needle stone	synonym of mesotype (see mesotype)
needle-tin	variety of **cassiterite**
nemalite	fibrous variety of **brucite**
nepheline	120 (silicates). Some localities change colour on exposure to light (reversible).
nephelite	synonym of **nepheline**
nephrite	massive, fine-grained variety of **actinolite** OR **tremolite**
niccolite	synonym of **nickeline**
nickel-skutterudite	02 (sulphides)

nickeline	02 (sulphides)
nitratine	synonym of **nitratite** (both names acceptable)
nitratite	18 (nitrates). Control humidity to prevent deliquescence.
nitre	18 (nitrates). Control humidity to prevent deliquescence.
nosean	120 (silicates)
octahedrite	synonym of **anatase**
okenite	100 (silicates). Fibrous; handle with care.
oligoclase	120 (silicates – FELDSPAR group)
olivenite	41 (phosphates, arsenates & vanadates). Often fibrous, handle with care.
olivine	70 (silicates – OLIVINE group)
OLIVINE group	70 (silicates)
omphacite	100 (silicates – PYROXENE group)
onyx marble (= oriental alabaster)	variety of **calcite**
onyx or *onyx-agate*	variety of **quartz** var. *chalcedony*
opal	60 (silica). Control humidity to prevent dehydration and shrinkage.
orangeite	variety of **thorite**
oriental alabaster (= onyx marble)	variety of **calcite**
oriental amethyst	purple gem variety of **corundum**; similarly, oriental emerald, oriental topaz for green and yellow-brown gem varieties respectively.
orpiment	02 (sulphides). Toxic.
orthite	synonym of **allanite**
orthoclase	120 (silicates – FELDSPAR group)
ottrelite	70 (silicates)
oxhaverite	synonym of APOPHYLLITE
pachnolite	11 (halides)
palygorskite	110 (silicates)
paragonite	110 (silicates – MICA group)
pargasite	100 (silicates – AMPHIBOLE group)
peacock ore	synonym of **bornite** OR **chalcopyrite** (usually the former)
pearl spar	synonym of **dolomite**
pectolite	100 (silicates)
pennantite	110 (silicates – CHLORITE group)
pennine or *penninite*	variety of **clinochlore**
pentlandite	02 (sulphides)
pericline	variety of **albite**
peridot	gem variety of OLIVINE
peristerite	variety of **albite**
perovskite	04 (oxides & hydroxides)
petalite	120 (silicates)
pharmacosiderite	42 (phosphates, arsenates & vanadates)
phenakite	70 (silicates). Some localities change colour on exposure to light.
phenacite	synonym of **phenakite**
phillipsite	120 (silicates – ZEOLITE group)
phlogopite	110 (silicates – MICA group)
phosgenite	16 (carbonates)

140

picrolite	variety of **antigorite**
piedmontite	synonym of **piemontite**
piemontite	80 (silicates)
pilolite	name applied to tough matted fibrous minerals (in part, synonymous with mountain leather or mountain cork), often **palygorskite**.
pistacite	synonym of **epidote**
pitchblende	variety of **uraninite**. Radioactive.
pitticite	43 (phosphates, arsenates & vanadates)
plagioclase	120 (silicates – FELDSPAR group) general name for FELDSPARS in the series **albite** to **anorthite**.
plasma	variety of **quartz** var. *chalcedony*
platinum	01 (elements & alloys)
pleonaste	synonym of *ceylonite*, a variety of **spinel**
plumbago	synonym of **graphite** OR **galena**
plumbogummite	42 (phosphates, arsenates & vanadates)
pollucite	120 (silicates)
polybasite	03 (sulphosalts). Keep in dark.
polycrase	08 (oxides & hydroxides). May be radioactive. Control humidity to prevent hydration.
polyhalite	29 (sulphates)
porcelain jasper	baked clay
potash feldspar	synonym of **orthoclase**
prase	variety of **quartz** var. *chalcedony*
prehnite	110 (silicates)
proustite	03 (sulphosalts). Keep in dark.
pseudomalachite	41 (phosphates, arsenates & vanadates)
psilomelane	06 (oxides & hydroxides) general name for mixed hard manganese oxides.
pyrargyrite	03 (sulphosalts). Keep in dark.
pyrite	02 (sulphides). Control humidity.
pyrites	synonym of **pyrite**
pyrochlore	08 (oxides & hydroxides). Control humidity to prevent hydration.
pyrolusite	04 (oxides & hydroxides)
pyromorphite	41 (phosphates, arsenates & vanadates)
pyrope	70 (silicates – GARNET group)
pyrophyllite	110 (silicates). Very soft, handle with care.
PYROSMALITE	110 (silicates) group name, includes **ferropyrosmalite** and **manganpyrosmalite**
PYROXENE	100 (silicates) group name
pyrrhite	synonym of **pyrochlore**
pyrrhotine	synonym of **pyrrhotite** (both names acceptable)
pyrrhotite	02 (sulphides). Control humidity.
quartz	60 (silica) varieties *amethyst*, *chrysoprase*, *rose quartz* and *smoky quartz* may fade in strong light.
quick silver	synonym of **mercury**
ralstonite	11 (halides)
rashleighite	variety of **turquoise**
realgar	02 (sulphides). Toxic. Keep in dark.

red cobalt	synonym of **erythrite**
red copper oxide	synonym of **cuprite**
red lead	synonym of **minium**
red lead ore	synonym of **crocoite**
red silver ore	synonym of **proustite** OR **pyrargyrite**
red zinc oxide	synonym of **zincite**
redruthite	synonym of **chalcocite**
rhaetizite	synonym of **kyanite**
rhodochrosite	14 (carbonates)
rhodonite	100 (silicates)
ribbon jasper	variety of **quartz** var. *chalcedony*
richterite	100 (silicates – AMPHIBOLE group)
riebeckite	100 (silicates – AMPHIBOLE group) asbestos: avoid inhalation, keep in sealed container.
ripidolite	variety of **clinochlore**
rockbridgeite	41 (phosphates, arsenates & vanadates)
rock crystal	colourless variety of **quartz**
rock salt	synonym of **halite**
rosasite	16 (carbonates)
roselite	40 (phosphates, arsenates & vanadates)
rose quartz	pink variety of **quartz**. May fade in strong light.
rubellan	variety of **biotite**
rubellite	pink or red variety of TOURMALINE
ruby	red gem variety of **corundum**
ruby blende	synonym of **sphalerite**
ruby copper ore	synonym of **cuprite**
ruby silver ore	synonym of **proustite** OR **pyrargyrite**
ruby-spinel	red gem variety of **spinel**
rutile	04 (oxides & hydroxides)
sahlite or salite	synonym of **diopside**
sal ammoniac	09 (halides)
saltpetre	synonym of **nitre**
samarskite	08 (oxides & hydroxides)
sanidine	120 (silicates – FELDSPAR group)
sapphire	gem variety of **corundum** – all colours except red. Unless the colour is blue, it should precede the word *sapphire*, eg *green sapphire, yellow sapphire, white* (ie colourless) *sapphire*.
sarcolite	120 (silicates)
sard	variety of **quartz** var. *chalcedony*
sardonyx	variety of **quartz** var. *chalcedony*
sassolite	24 (borates)
satin-spar	variety of **gypsum** OR **calcite** OR **aragonite**
SCAPOLITE	120 (silicates) group name
scheelite	48 (chromates, molybdates & tungstates)
schorl	90 (silicates – TOURMALINE group) see TOURMALINE
schweizerite	synonym of **antigorite**
scolecite	120 (silicates – ZEOLITE group). Fibrous crystals, handle with care.

scorodite	40 (phosphates, arsenates & vanadates)
selenite	variety of **gypsum**
senarmontite	04 (oxides & hydroxides). Toxic.
sepiolite	110 (silicates)
sericite	fine-grained variety of **muscovite**, usually with illite
SERPENTINE	110 (silicates) group name, or a synonym for 'serpentinite', a rock composed predominantly of SERPENTINE minerals.
siderite	14 (carbonates)
silicified coral	**quartz** var. *chalcedony*, replacing coral
silicified sponge	**quartz** var. *chalcedony*, replacing sponge
silicified wood	**quartz** var. *chalcedony* OR **opal**, replacing wood
sillimanite	70 (silicates)
silver	01 (elements & alloys). Readily tarnishes.
silver glance	synonym of **argentite OR acanthite**
skutterudite	02 (sulphides)
smaltite	variety of **skutterudite**
smithsonite	14 (carbonates)
smoky quartz	smoky-brown variety of **quartz**. May fade in strong light.
sodalite	120 (silicates). Some localities change colour on exposure to light.
soda nitre	synonym of **nitratine**
sparable tin	variety of **cassiterite**
sparry iron	synonym of **siderite**
spectrolite	gem name for iridescent **labradorite**
spessartine	70 (silicates – GARNET group)
spessartite	synonym of **spessartine**
sphalerite	02 (sulphides)
sphene	synonym of **titanite**
spherocobaltite	14 (carbonates). Toxic.
spinel	07 (oxides & hydroxides)
spodumene	100 (silicates – PYROXENE group)
stannite	02 (sulphides). Readily tarnishes.
star-ruby, *star-sapphire*, *star-quartz*, *star-diopside* (and other species).	varieties of **corundum**, **quartz**, **diopside** etc showing 'asterism', a star-shaped play of light due to the presence of symmetrically arranged inclusions.
staurolite	70 (silicates)
steatite	massive, fine-grained variety of **talc**
stephanite	03 (sulphosalts). Keep in dark.
stibarsen	01 (elements & alloys)
stibnite	02 (sulphides). Toxic. Readily tarnishes, keep in dark.
stilbite	120 (silicates – ZEOLITE group)
stream tin	variety of **cassiterite**
strengite	40 (phosphates, arsenates & vanadates)
strontianite	14 (carbonates)
sulphur	01 (elements & alloys). Toxic. Fluctuations in temperature, even that caused by handling, can cause shattering. Avoid handling.
sunstone	variety of **oligoclase**
sylvanite	02 (sulphides). Keep in dark.

sylvine	synonym of **sylvite** (both names acceptable)
sylvite	09 (halides). Control humidity to prevent deliquescence.
talc	110 (silicates). Very soft, handle with care.
tantalite	08 (oxides & hydroxides)
tanzanite	blue gem variety of **zoisite**
tellurobismuthite	02 (sulphides)
tennantite	03 (sulphosalts)
tenorite	04 (oxides & hydroxides). Toxic.
tetradymite	02 (sulphides)
tetrahedrite	03 (sulphosalts)
thomsenolite	11 (halides)
thomsonite	120 (silicates – ZEOLITE group)
thorite	70 (silicates)
thuringite	variety of **chamosite**
tiger-eye	variety of **quartz**
tile-ore	variety of **cuprite**
tin ore	synonym of **cassiterite**
tin pyrites	synonym of **stannite**
titanite	70 (silicates)
topaz	70 (silicates). Some localities change colour on exposure to light.
topazolite	variety of **andradite**
torbernite	40 (phosphates, arsenates & vanadates). May be radioactive.
TOURMALINE	90 (silicates) group name, includes **dravite**, **elbaite** and **schorl**
tremolite	100 (silicates – AMPHIBOLE group) asbestos: avoid inhalation, keep in sealed container.
tridymite	60 (silica)
triplite	41 (phosphates, arsenates & vanadates). Control humidity to prevent hydration.
trona	13 (carbonates). Control humidity to prevent efflorescence.
turnerite	synonym of **monazite**
turquoise	42 (phosphates, arsenates & vanadates). May fade on exposure to light. Control humidity to prevent dehydration and shrinkage.
ulexite	26 (borates)
uranic mica	discredited synonym of uranite (see uranite)
uraninite	05 (oxides & hydroxides). Radioactive.
uranite	group name for phosphates and arsenates of uranium with alkali earth elements or copper.
uvarovite	70 (silicates – GARNET group)
valentinite	04 (oxides & hydroxides). Toxic.
vanadinite	41 (phosphates, arsenates & vanadates). Bright yellow specimens turn dull brown on exposure to light.
variscite	40 (phosphates, arsenates & vanadates)
varlamoffite	variety of **cassiterite**
vermiculite	110 (silicates)
vesuvianite	80 (silicates)

violan or violane	variety of **diopside** OR **augite**
vivianite	40 (phosphates, arsenates & vanadates). Turns from colourless to blue-black and can disintegrate on exposure to light. Keep in dark.
wad	06 (oxides & hydroxides) general term for mixed soft manganese oxides
wavellite	42 (phosphates, arsenates & vanadates)
wernerite	synonym of SCAPOLITE
white lead ore	synonym of **cerussite**
willemite	70 (silicates)
witherite	14 (carbonates). Toxic.
wöhlerite	80 (silicates)
wolframite	48 (molybdates & tungstates)
wollastonite	100 (silicates)
wood-copper	variety of **olivenite**
wood goethite	variety of **goethite**
wood-tin	variety of **cassiterite**
woodwardite	31 (sulphates)
wulfenite	48 (molybdates & tungstates)
wurtzite	02 (sulphides)
xenotime	38 (phosphates, arsenates & vanadates)
yellow copper ore	synonym of **chalcopyrite**
yellow ochre	synonym of limonite (see limonite)
zaratite	16 (carbonates)
ZEOLITE	120 (silicates) group name
zinc blende	synonym of **sphalerite**
zinc spinel	synonym of **gahnite**
zincite	04 (oxides & hydroxides)
zinkenite	03 (sulphosalts)
zinnwaldite	110 (silicates – MICA group)
zircon	70 (silicates). Some localities change colour on exposure to light.
zirconolite	synonym of **zirkelite**
zoisite	80 (silicates)
zorgite	02 (sulphides & sulphosalts) mixture of **clausthalite**, **umangite** and **tiemannite**

Merchandise

Most 'geological' merchandise seems to consist of plastic dinosaurs, which are actually very popular indeed! But there is much more available. Think about:

- Pencils, rubbers and other cheap souvenirs with the local fossil on them.
- Postcards. It is best to choose local subjects if possible. Try the British Geological Survey, the British Museum (Natural History), the Geological Museum, London, and nearby larger museums. Alternatively you can produce your own at some commercial risk: consider old quarry photos, etchings, watercolours and landscapes as well as the usual fossils and minerals. The BGS photo library may have suitable pictures.
- Colour transparencies are probably not worth commissioning or producing for sale in the shop unless you can find a ready-made supply. Check the same sources as for postcards. If the subject is a local scenic landmark slides may already be available. If you want some for your own use, eg in lectures, it may be worth trying the BGS photo library.
- Posters. The BGS and the British Museum (Natural History) sell a selection.
- Models. There is a wide range of different types (card, plastic and wood) especially of dinosaurs, mammoths, plesiosaurs and so on. A source of good quality solid models is Invicta Plastics, Oadby, Leicester. Dominion Toys Ltd, Unit 3, Richmar Estate, Butts Pond, Sturminster Newton, Dorset DT10 1AZ, import 'Battat' slot-together wooden skeletal models, and also plastic skeletal models including a flying model pterodactyl, *Pterosaurus*. Cut-out card models are available from several suppliers.
- Replicas and casts are the only practical and ethical way of selling or making available for handling some rare fossils, such as dinosaur teeth or pterosaur skeletons. However, they do not give the same feel as the real item. There is a large range available from Stuart Baldwin, Fossil Hall, Boars Tye Road, Silver End, Witham, Essex CM8 3QA.
- Real fossils and minerals should not be sold in the museum shop without careful thought and perhaps discussion with a specialist curator. There are several pitfalls, especially the risks of purchasing illicitly collected material, or of encouraging overcollection. People may think you are selling the collections, and donors may want payment. But selling fossils can serve an educational role in the broadest sense.

  Many people do like to have a real specimen of their own, especially if they can't collect it themselves, or process it, such as an ammonite cut and polished to show the interior. Locally collected material should not normally be sold unless it is really common and the payment is mainly to cover the costs of processing.

Useful addresses

Area Museum Services

Area Museum Council for the South West, Hestercombe House, Cheddon Fitz-paine, Taunton TA2 8LQ, (0823) 259696

Area Museums Service for South Eastern England, Ferroners House, Barbican, London EC2Y 8AA, 01-600 0219

Council of Museums in Wales, 32 Park Place, Cardiff CF1 3BA, (0222) 225432

East Midlands Area Museum Service, Courtyard Buildings, Wollaton Park, Nottingham NG8 2AE, (0602) 288749

North of England Museums Service, House of Recovery, Bath Lane, Newcastle upon Tyne NE4 5SQ

North West Museum and Art Gallery Service, Griffin Lodge, Griffin Park, Blackburn BB2 2PN, (0254) 670211

Scottish Museums Council, County House, 20–22 Torphichen Street, Edinburgh EH3 8JB, 031-229 7465

West Midlands Area Museum Service, Hanbury Road, Stoke Prior, Bromsgrove, Worcestershire B60 4AD, (0527) 72258

Yorkshire and Humberside Museums Council, Farnley Hall, Hall Lane, Leeds LS12 5HA, (0532) 638909

Geology

British Geological Survey, Keyworth, Nottingham NG12 5GG

British Museum (Natural History), Cromwell Road, London SW7 5BD

The Geological Curators' Group:
  Simon Knell, Secretary, Scunthorpe Museum, Oswald Road, Scunthorpe DN15 7BD, (0724) 843533
  Tom Sharpe, Treasurer/Membership Secretary, Geology Department, National Museum of Wales, Cathays Park, Cardiff CF1 3NP, (0222) 397951
  Diana Smith, 'Thumbs Up' Campaign Coordinator, Haslemere Educational Museum, High Street, Haslemere, Surrey GU27 2LA
  CING: Michael Taylor, GCG Recorder, Earth Sciences Section, Leicestershire Museums Service, 96 New Walk, Leicester LE1 6TD, (0533) 554100
  The Geological Curator: P R Crowther, Editor, City of Bristol Museum and Art Gallery, Queen's Road, Bristol BS8 1RL

Geological Museum, Exhibition Road, London SW7 2DE

The Geological Society, Burlington House, Piccadilly, London W1V 0JU

The Geologists' Association, Burlington House, Piccadilly, London W1V 0JU

Geology Today
  P J Smith, Editor, 32 St James Close, Hanslope, Milton Keynes MK19 7LF
  Subscriptions: Blackwell Scientific Publications, Osney Mead, Oxford

Institution of Geologists, Burlington House, Piccadilly, London W1V 9HG
National Scheme for Geological Site Documentation
   Mick Stanley, Coordinator, c/o Derbyshire Museums Service, John Turner House, Parkway, Darley Dale, Matlock DE4 2FW, (0629) 733226

Sponsorship and Funding

Area Museum Services

The Geological Society

The Geologists' Association

The Museums and Galleries Commission, 7 St James' Square, London SW1Y 4JU

National Heritage Memorial Fund, Church House, Great Smith Street, London SW1P 3BL

National Museums of Scotland Grant-in-Aid Fund for the Preservation of Scientific and Technological Material, Director, Royal Museum of Scotland, Chambers Street, Edinburgh EH1 1JF

The National Trust, 36–38 Queen Anne's Square, London SW1H 9AS

National Trust for Scotland, 5 Charlotte Square, Edinburgh EH2

Nature Conservancy Council, Northminster House, Peterborough PE1 1UA

The Royal Society, 6 Carlton House Terrace, London SW1Y 5AG

Science Museum Grant-in-Aid Fund, Science Museum, Exhibition Road, London SW7 2DD

Documentation

Area Museum Services

Museums' Computer Group: Jonathan Moffett (Chairman), Ashmolean Museum, Beaumont Street, Oxford OX1 2PH

Museum Documentation Association, Building O, 347 Cherry Hinton Road, Cambridge CB1 4DH

Picture libraries

Ardea, 35 Brodrick Road, Wandsworth Common, London SW17

Bruce Coleman Ltd, 17 Windsor Street, Uxbridge UB8 1AB

Education

Association for Science Education: College Lane, Hatfield, Herts AL10 9AA

Association of Teachers in Geology: Mrs J Pendry, Membership Secretary, 22 Mountsfield Close, Newport Pagnell, Bucks MK16 0JE

Group for Education in Museums: Jeni Harrison, Membership Secretary, 389 Great Western Road, Aberdeen AB1 6NY

Workers' Educational Association: Temple House, 9 Upper Berkeley Street, London W1H 8BY

148

Index

Printed in the United Kingdom for Her Majesty's Stationery Office
Dd. 240066   5/89   C25   44849